Published by:
Novel Units, Inc.
P.O. Box 791610
San Antonio, TX 78279

Graphic Organizer

Collection

Contributions by:
Mary Dennis
Phyllis Green
Gloria Levine
Anne Troy

Editor:
Phyllis Green

ISBN 1-56137-783-X

©1999, 2000 Novel Units, Inc.
All rights reserved. Printed in the
United States of America.

Graphic Organizers: An Overview

Graphic organizers are visual representations of how ideas are related to each other. These "pictures"—including Venn diagrams, flow charts, attribute webs, etc.—help students collect information, make interpretations, solve problems, devise plans, and become aware of how they think.

The theoretical basis for graphic organizers lies in learning theory and particularly in these ideas:

> Focusing on important concepts and omitting extraneous details helps the student see how concepts are related and makes them more easily understood.
>
> The human mind stores information in an orderly fashion, creating schemas. New information is more easily assimilated if prior knowledge is retrieved and the existing schema provides a ready framework for new information.
>
> Graphic organizers, as visual pictures, are mental tools which help the learner remember.
>
> Using graphic organizers and thereby connecting visual language with verbal language is active learning.

Graphic organizers are also called semantic maps, mind maps, structured overviews, webs, concept maps, semantic organizers. The schema of the organizer can be **hierarchical**, with levels and subsets. **Conceptual** organizers take a central idea or concept and branch out from it. **Sequential** organizers focus on the order, chronology, or flow of the ideas. **Cyclical** organizers form a pattern in a circular fashion.

When teachers introduce graphic organizers into their instruction, they need to model the use of the organizer several times before asking students to use the organizers independently. The modeling can be with a large wall chart, an overhead transparency, or a drawing on the chalkboard. Using those props, the teacher talks the students through thinking in the graphic manner and recording ideas on the organizer. The next step is to generate the ideas with a general class participation strategy. Cooperative groups can further reinforce the organizer's use, followed by individual use.

Graphic organizers can be used for assessment. Once students have used graphic organizers with a piece of literature or unit of study, their mastery of that use can be tested by asking students to use the graphic organizer on new material, either library books or the next novel to be read or with a shortened selection from another book or from another work by the same author. Student thinking in organizing their approach to literature can be tested by asking them to apply a new or different graphic organizer with the literature just completed.

This Graphic Organizer Collection includes five sections, each with a short narrative explanation on that particular organizer: Advance Organizers, Character Analysis Graphics, Story Maps, Comprehension Strategies, and Assessment. Choosing from the many organizers included in the teacher's guides from the Novel Units' line of educational products, the author has selected 58 graphics. These 58 pages can be duplicated for use with any single class. The perforated pages allow easy access to the duplicator.

Samples of completed organizers are included in each section.

Advance Organizers

Advance organizers are frameworks used to help students pull up prior knowledge and prepare to study something new. Here are some advance organizer ideas:

1. Anticipation Guide: Students discuss themes and ideas which they will meet in a story or textbook or instructional unit.

2. Nonfiction review of "the facts" of the setting, the times and places they will encounter in a piece of literature. The review can and should include print matter, pictures, songs and sounds, and auditory materials.

3. Predicting about a story not only prepares students for a particular story, but models the comprehension strategy.

4. K-W-L: Students complete the first two columns of a chart, noting what they "know" about a topic and what they "want" to learn (phrased in question form). The third column is completed at the conclusion of the instructional module to record what they've "learned."

What They Know	What They Would Like to Know	What They Learned

5. A variation of the K-W-L chart can focus on a book's characters, recording what students know of a character's heritage and culture and what questions they'd like answered. The third column records what they've learned and is completed after reading.

6. Role Play: Have students improvise skits about situations analogous to what happens in a piece of literature or an experiment or situation to be studied (as in, for example, a discovery or a trip to the moon).

7. Prereading Journal or Illustration: Free-write or free-draw for ten minutes, nonstop, beginning with ideas from prereading discussion or role play.

8. Display significant objects from a story or instructional unit to promote predicting.

Notes From My Use of Advance Organizers

Name _____

Need-to-Know Chart

Directions: Chapter-by-chapter, fill in the Before Reading—What I hope to learn from column. Then read the chapter and after reading, fill in the After Reading—What I now know column.

Before Reading	After Reading
What I hope to learn from:	What I now know:
Chapter _____:	
Chapter _____:	
Chapter _____:	
Chapter _____:	
Chapter _____:	
Chapter _____:	
Chapter _____:	

Need-to-Know Chart for *Canyons* by Gary Paulsen

Directions: Chapter-by-chapter, fill in the Before Reading—What I hope to learn from column. Then read the chapter and after reading, fill in the After Reading—What I now know column.

Before Reading	After Reading
What I hope to learn from:	What I now know:
Chapter 1: *the storyteller, the point of view*	
Chapter 2: *the main characters, why there's no title for the chapter*	
Chapter 3: *how Coyote Runs proves he's a man*	
Chapter 4: *how Brennan earns money*	
Chapter 5: *how nineteenth century Indians conducted raiding parties*	
Chapter 6: *whether Brennan is similar to my friends*	
Chapter 7: *What are Visions and how do they fit into this book?*	

Teacher Notes

The Need-to-Know Chart can be used with any reading activity. The chart requires the student to note a purpose for reading chapter-by-chapter. The second column offers a place to summarize and take stock.

Clue Log

Directions: When you read something you think might be important later on, write it down. See if you can solve the book's mystery.

Page	Clue (event or item)	Could Have Something To Do With:

Clue Log for
The Bodies in the Bessledorf Hotel by Phyllis Reynolds Naylor

Directions: When you read something you think might be important later on, write it down. See if you can solve the book's mystery.

Page	Clue (event or item)	Could Have Something To Do With:
1-2	detail about the number of people staying in the hotel	perhaps there will be multiple bodies as the title suggests
9	no water in the tub and body gone	whether the cleaning woman had actually seen the body
12	Mixed Blessing didn't like Mr. Gusset	dead man was anti-dog, evil, unfriendly, a cat-lover
12	Mr. Gusset had one case when he checked in	perhaps the killer wanted the case
12	Bernie's parents didn't tell Officer Feeney they'd argued about Mr. Gusset	Bernie's parents' involvement and/or knowledge

Teacher Notes

This page is tailored for mysteries. Teachers can also adapt the page for any observation and discovery activity. In such instances, students record observa-tions in the "clue" column and put a supposition, idea, or theory in the second column. Such double use of the page suggests some integrated instructional possibilities.

Name _____

 ## Clue Search for

_____

Directions: Collect information about the book for each of the checked items. Write it down and then make some predictions for the book.

Source of Hints About the Book	Information Provided
☑ Dedication	
☑ Title	
☑ Cover illustration	
☑ Teasers on the book cover or in the book jacket	
☑ Recommendations of friends	
☑ Recommendations of reviewers/ awards won	

Your predictions for the book:

Clue Search for

The Upstairs Room by Johanna Reiss

Directions: Collect information about the book for each of the checked items. Write it down and then make some predictions for the book.

Source of Hints About the Book	Information Provided
☑ Dedication	*book is autobiographical*
☑ Title	*location*
☑ Cover illustration	*female protagonists* *Nazi Flag*
☑ Teasers on the book cover or in the book jacket	*admirable account*
☑ Recommendations of friends	
☑ Recommendations of reviewers/ awards won	*School Library Journal Best Book of the Year*

Your predictions for the book: *Could this be a Diary of Anne Frank kind of book? Is it set during World War II?*

Teacher Notes

This page focuses on a book—either a piece of children's literature or a text book or any other book a student might read. The student physically interacts with the written word and is reminded of the clues a book offers.

Name _____

Getting the "Lay of the Land"

Directions: Prepare for reading by answering the following short-answer questions.

1. Who is the author?

    _____

2. What does the title suggest to you about the book?

    _____

    _____

    _____

    _____

3. When was the book written?

    _____

4. How many pages are there in the book?

    _____

5. Thumb through the book. Read three pages—one from near the beginning, one from near the middle, and one from near the end. What predictions do you make about the book?

    _____

    _____

    _____

    _____

6. What does the cover suggest to you about the book?

    _____

    _____

    _____

    _____

Getting the "Lay of the Land" for
Charlotte's Web by E. B. White

Directions: Prepare for reading by answering the following short-answer questions.

1. Who is the author?

   E. B. White

2. What does the title suggest to you about the book?

   a spider and someone named Charlotte

3. When was the book written?

   copyright is 1952—prior to that

4. How many pages are there in the book?

   184 pages

5. Thumb through the book. Read three pages—one from near the beginning, one from near the middle, and one from near the end. What predictions do you make about the book?

   There are pictures of farm scenes and spider webs. This is fantasy—animals talk.

6. What does the cover suggest to you about the book?

   A lamb, pig, and duck as well as a girl figure in the story. It's set on a farm.

Teacher Notes

This page is a series of generic questions to help get ready to read a book. Though not strictly speaking a graphic organizer, it is included as an organizer and can be used with a variety of books.

Be a Detective!

Directions: Check out the book by looking at the cover, thumbing through the pages. Then, ask yourself who, what, where, when, why, and how. Put your questions in the spaces below. Your teacher will redistribute your questions to another student to find the answers. Alternatively, check out an experiment or picture or group of objects or ideas or content area. Then write the six questions.

How?
_____
_____
_____
_____

Where?
_____
_____
_____

What?
_____
_____
_____

Who?
_____
_____
_____
_____

Why?
_____
_____
_____
_____

When?
_____
_____
_____
_____

Be a Detective! for *Maniac Magee* by Jerry Spinelli

Directions: Check out the book by looking at the cover, thumbing through the pages. Then, ask yourself who, what, where, when, why, and how. Put your questions in the spaces below. Your teacher will redistribute your questions to another student to find the answers. Alternatively, check out an experiment or picture or group of objects or ideas or content area. Then write the six questions.

How?
How do worn running shoes figure in the book?

Who?
Who is on the cover? Male? Maybe female? How old?

Where?
Where is the book book set? How does the brick wall on the cover figure into it?

Why?
Why does the book have three sections?

What?
What is the Newbery Medal?

When?
When does the story take place? Contemporary?

Teacher Notes

The question prompts help students form questions. Redis-tributing the questions to other students provides some control for quality and discourages some silliness in answering. The page can be completed col-laboratively by a small coop-erative group.

The prompts work well across the curriculum. It is partic-ularly interesting to use for math where a number/word interface is set up.

Anticipation Guide

Directions: For each of the statements, choose a response from the scale below. Share your answers by discussing them with a partner. After you have finished reading and studying the book, you might want to take this quiz again and compare your new answers with your original ones.

-5	-3	0	+3	+5
Disagree Strongly	Disagree Somewhat	No Opinion	Agree Somewhat	Agree Strongly

_____ 1. _____

_____

_____ 2. _____

_____

_____ 3. _____

_____

_____ 4. _____

_____

_____ 5. _____

_____

_____ 6. _____

_____

_____ 7. _____

_____

_____ 8. _____

_____

_____ 9. _____

_____

© Novel Units, Inc.

15

Anticipation Guide for *A Separate Peace* by John Knowles

Directions: For each of the statements, choose a response from the scale below. Share your answers by discussing them with a partner. After you have finished reading and studying the book, you might want to take this quiz again and compare your new answers with your original ones.

-5	-3	0	+3	+5
Disagree Strongly	Disagree Somewhat	No Opinion	Agree Somewhat	Agree Strongly

_____ 1. *True friends never lie to one another.*

_____ 2. *Jealousy is common between good friends.*

_____ 3. *Almost everyone must fight some kind of battle.*

_____ 4. *It's best to confess your mistakes right away.*

_____ 5. *Nagging guilt can affect how a person lives his or her life.*

_____ 6. *True friendship is forever; you should always forgive a friend, no matter what he or she has done.*

_____ 7. *It is important to me to conform to school rules.*

_____ 8. *It is important to me to express my individuality.*

_____ 9. *Part of friendship consists of accepting a friend's shortcomings.*

Teacher Notes

"Statements" which teachers must provide will vary with the particular book or instruction. "Statements" can 1) state common general attitudes which students will bring to the learning situation, 2) reflect important themes in the book, 3) intrigue the student by challenging his own world and feelings.

Uses across the curriculum:

Social Studies: Can address and challenge common inaccuracies in history or sociology.

Mathematics: Stress new concepts to be taught.

Science: State laws and principles to be taught.

Prereading Knowledge Chart

Directions: In the space provided, mark each statement true or false based on what you think now. Read the book to see if you are correct.

_____ 1. _____

_____

_____ 2. _____

_____

_____ 3. _____

_____

_____ 4. _____

_____

_____ 5. _____

_____

_____ 6. _____

_____

_____ 7. _____

_____

_____ 8. _____

_____

_____ 9. _____

_____

_____ 10. _____

_____

_____ 11. _____

_____

Prereading Knowledge Chart from
My Side of the Mountain by Jean Craighead George

Directions: In the space provided, mark each statement true or false based on what you think now. Read the book to see if you are correct.

_____ 1. Winters in the Catskills are usually mild, with the proximity to the seashore keeping snowfall down.

_____ 2. It is a myth that birds can be used to detect poisonous carbon monoxide.

_____ 3. Falcons are hawks that can be trained to hunt prey such as rabbits for humans.

_____ 4. No wild mushrooms are edible.

_____ 5. You can eat puffballs and dogtooth violet bulbs.

_____ 6. Great horned owls live in the Catskills.

_____ 7. Grizzly bears sometimes bother farmers in New York.

_____ 8. Walnuts and hazelnuts grow wild in the Catskills.

_____ 9. Wild strawberries grow year-round in Delhi, New York.

_____ 10. In a fight, a hawk would probably kill a weasel.

_____ 11. Deer are among the few animals that have no cry.

Teacher Notes

Prereading knowledge is addressed in literary units with a lot of "facts." In these cases students will learn "hard content" while reading a good story. When using multi media like videos and audios and CD roms, this page can be an effective beginning and ending activity to prepare and then to cement new learning. With any true-false exercise, it is important to give corrected statements lest students remember incorrect ideas.

A Character's World

Directions: You may be able to draw parallels between a character's world and your own. Think about each item on the top. Then describe a related situation or event from your own world on the bottom.

_____'s World
_____
_____
_____

My World
_____
_____

_____'s World
_____
_____
_____

My World
_____
_____

_____'s World
_____
_____
_____

My World
_____
_____

_____'s World
_____
_____
_____

My World
_____
_____

A Character's World for *The Outsiders* by S. E. Hinton

Directions: You may be able to draw parallels between a character's world and your own. Think about each item on the top. Then describe a related situation or event from your own world on the bottom.

Ponyboy's World

Greasers can't walk alone too much or they'll get jumped.

My World

Ponyboy's World

When you grow up in a tight-knit neighborhood like ours, you get to know each other real well.

My World

Ponyboy's World

Organized gangs are rarities—they are just small bunches of friends who stick together.

My World

Ponyboy's World

Darry can get drunk in a drag race or dancing without ever getting near alcohol. He gets drunk on just plain living.

My World

Teacher Notes

The idea here is to allow students to make comparisons and to make the new information their own—to personalize.

KWL

Directions: As the book or content area is studied, fill in this chart. Before reading review what you KNOW (about the setting and background) in the **K** column. The **W** column is for questions you expect to have answered. The **L** column is completed after reading to list what you have learned.

K	W	L

KWL

Directions: As the book or content area is studied, fill in this chart. Before reading review what you KNOW (about the setting and background) in the **K** column. The **W** column is for questions you expect to have answered. The **L** column is completed after reading to list what you have learned.

K	W	L

Teacher Notes

The student answers will vary widely. In the "K" column, look for volume of ideas as well as reasonable accuracy. Some of the "K" entries may later be disproved with the study. Once the "W" questions are generated, students can be challenged to suggest appropriate references and approaches to answer. If all the questions are not answered in the study, a fourth column "Y"—yet to answer— may be added.

Character Analysis Graphics

Character analysis graphics focus student attention on a book's characters, their particular demographic identification, the challenges of their life situations, and the ways they resolve their own peculiar problems. Characters are often the most memorable parts of books and the character analysis organizers help students to see the various aspects of character which the best of authors give to us.

The reading writing connection is particularly vivid with these organizers. The reader sees how the author uses words to provide for the reader a picture of the unique people in a particular book. Readers can identify, assess, and note similarities and differences from the people of their own lives.

The character analysis graphics can be,

1. Used as advance organizers before reading to predict ideas and increase interest;

2. Completed as the book is read to record new insights about characters;

3. Completed after reading to summarize and celebrate learning.

Attribute Webs

Attribute webs are simply a visual representation of a character's traits. They provide a systematic way for students to organize and recap the information they have about that particular character. Attribute webs may be used after reading the story or completed gradually as information unfolds—done individually, or finished as a group project.

One type of character web uses these categories:

→ How a character acts and feels (What do his/her statements reveal about feelings? What does his/her behavior show you about him/her? In a play—what do the character's gestures, facial expressions, tone of voice tell you about his/her emotions?)

→ How a character looks (What do clothing and physique tell you about this character?)

→ Where a character lives (In what country, state, neighborhood, does this character live? During what time period?)

→ How others feel about the character (What do others' statements and actions show about their attitude toward the character?)

In group discussion about the student attribute webs for specific characters, the teacher can ask for supportive evidence from the story.

Attribute webs need not be confined to characters. They can also be used to organize information about a concept, object, or place.

Attribute webs are a kind of semantic mapping. Students can move on from attribute webs to other creative kinds of mapping. They can be encouraged to modify attribute webs—use subdivisions, add divisions, change connections—in whatever ways are useful to them personally. It is important to emphasize that attribute webs are just a graphic way to record ideas. They provide students with a tool for helping them generate ideas and think about relationships among them.

Name _____

Attribute Web

Directions: The attribute web below is designed to help you gather clues the author provides about what a character is like. Fill in the blanks with words and phrases which tell how the character acts and looks, as well as what the character says and feels.

Acts ·················

1) _____

_____

2) _____

_____

3) _____

_____

4) _____

_____

Feels ················

1) _____

_____

2) _____

_____

3) _____

_____

4) _____

_____

Looks ···············

1) _____

_____

2) _____

_____

3) _____

_____

4) _____

_____

Says ················

1) _____

_____

2) _____

_____

3) _____

_____

4) _____

_____

Attribute Web for Alastor from *The Castle in the Attic*

Directions: The attribute web below is designed to help you gather clues the author provides about what a character is like. Fill in the blanks with words and phrases which tell how the character acts and looks, as well as what the character says and feels.

Acts • • • • • • • • • • • • • •

1) Dictatorial

2) Turns people into lead toys

3) Brings on drought and poor crops

4) _____

Feels • • • • • • • • • • • • • •

1) Lonely

2) Hated

3) _____

4) _____

ALASTOR

Looks • • • • • • • • • • • • • •

1) Old man (page 141)

2) Dressed in silver robe (page 141)

3) Thin gray matted hair (page 141)

4) Wary eyes (pages 141-142)

Says • • • • • • • • • • • • • •

1) Threatens

2) "I control you." (page 150)

3) Others fear and hate him

4) Screams at his subjects

Teacher Notes

Using the numbered lines directs students to give you the four best or most representative answers.

Name _____

Attribute Web

Directions: Fill in the ovals to indicate what the author has revealed about your chosen character.

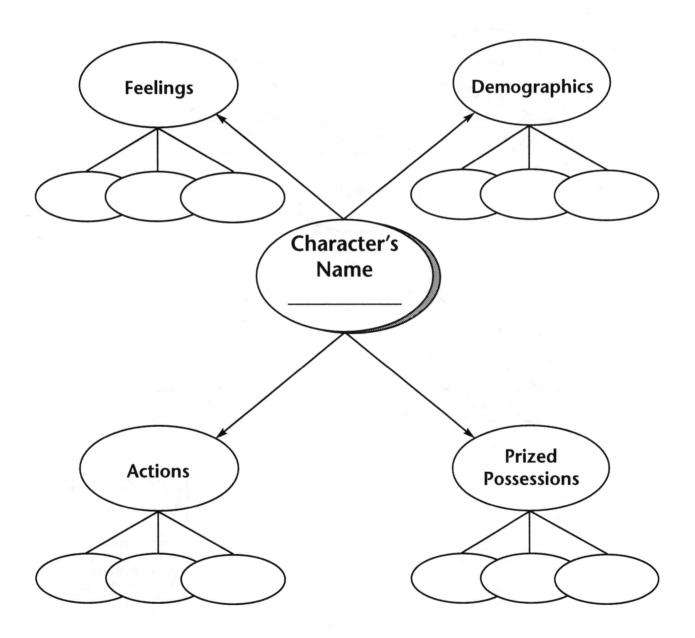

Attribute Web for William from
The Castle in the Attic

Directions: Fill in the ovals to indicate what the author has revealed about your chosen character.

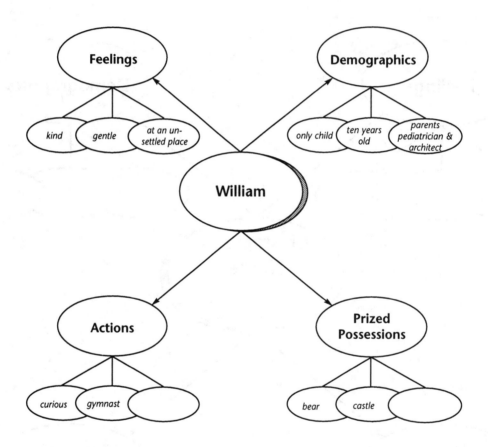

Feelings: kind, gentle, at an un-settled place

Demographics: only child, ten years old, parents pediatrician & architect

William

Actions: curious, gymnast

Prized Possessions: bear, castle

Teacher Notes

You may ask students for as many responses as they can "dream up" or limit them to the three or four best or most relevant ideas.

Attribute Web

Directions: Select a character from the book to tell about using the blocks below. Choose five of the blocks to answer.

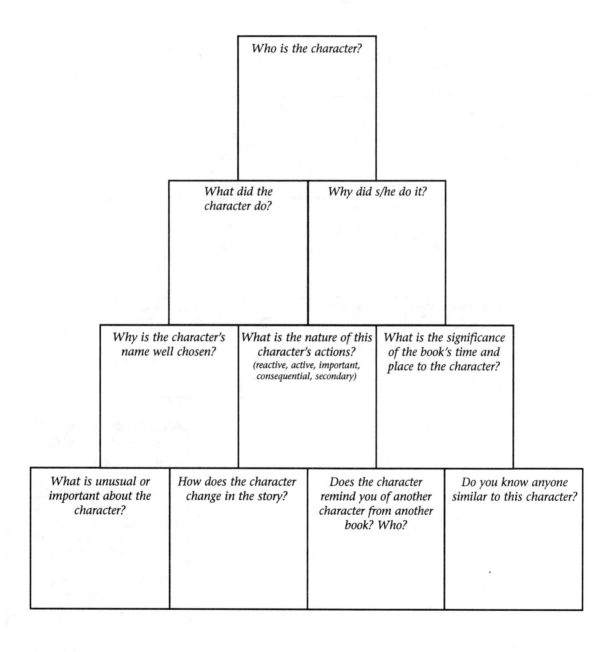

Attribute Web for Marty from *Shiloh*

Directions: Select a character from the book to tell about using the blocks below. Choose five of the blocks to answer.

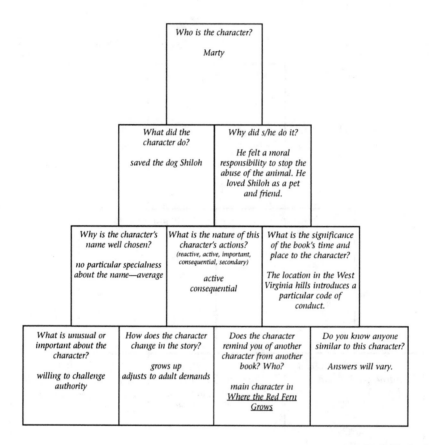

Who is the character?	
Marty	

What did the character do?	Why did s/he do it?
saved the dog Shiloh	He felt a moral responsibility to stop the abuse of the animal. He loved Shiloh as a pet and friend.

Why is the character's name well chosen?	What is the nature of this character's actions? (reactive, active, important, consequential, secondary)	What is the significance of the book's time and place to the character?
no particular specialness about the name—average	active consequential	The location in the West Virginia hills introduces a particular code of conduct.

What is unusual or important about the character?	How does the character change in the story?	Does the character remind you of another character from another book? Who?	Do you know anyone similar to this character?
willing to challenge authority	grows up adjusts to adult demands	main character in *Where the Red Fern Grows*	Answers will vary.

Teacher Notes

Students may suggest additional or different blocks for a particular book or character. Evidence for each answer can be requested.

A follow-up to this exercise can be a multi-paragraph descrip-tive essay on the character.

Note that the directions ask students to respond to five of the blocks. Extra responses could be extra credit.

Name _____

Attribute Web

Directions: Within each box, record evidence about the character.

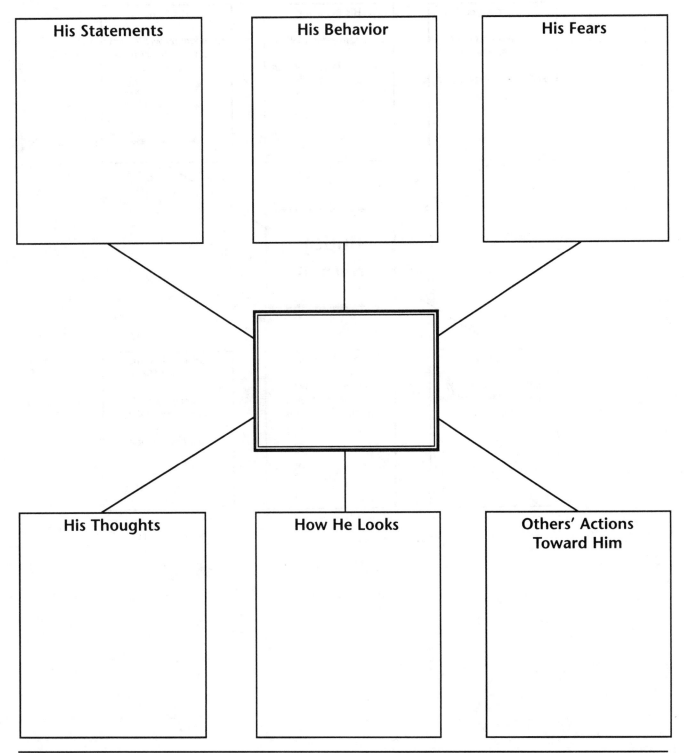

His Statements

His Behavior

His Fears

His Thoughts

How He Looks

Others' Actions
Toward Him

Attribute Web for Buddy Rankin from

Let the Circle Be Unbroken

Directions: Within each box, record evidence about the character.

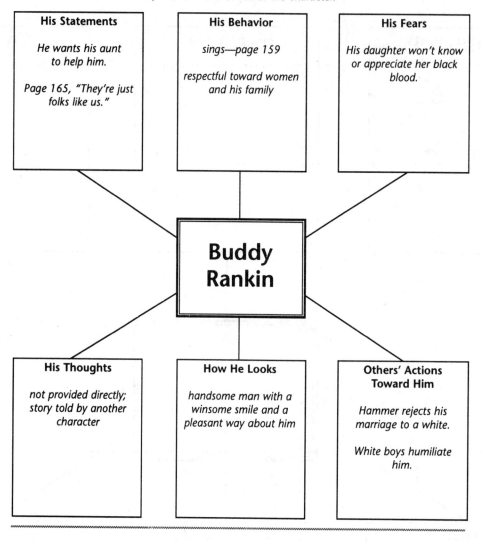

His Statements

He wants his aunt
to help him.

Page 165, "They're just
folks like us."

His Behavior

sings—page 159

respectful toward women
and his family

His Fears

His daughter won't know
or appreciate her black
blood.

Buddy Rankin

His Thoughts

not provided directly;
story told by another
character

How He Looks

handsome man with a
winsome smile and a
pleasant way about him

**Others' Actions
Toward Him**

Hammer rejects his
marriage to a white.

White boys humiliate
him.

Name _____

Attribute Web

Directions: Choose five characters from the book. List their names in the left hand boxes. Fill in the other boxes with the requested information.

Character	One Word Description	Appearance	Significance to the Story	Do you know anyone similar?

Suggested Answers

Attribute Web for characters from
Let the Circle Be Unbroken

Directions: Choose five characters from the book. List their names in the left hand boxes. Fill in the other boxes with the requested information.

Character	One Word Description	Appearance	Significance to the Story	Do you know anyone similar?
Suzella Rankin	appealing	attractive; "could pass" multiracial	introduces problems of multiracial people in the 1930's	
Deputy Haynes	prejudiced	no details provided	does his job, bringing his own preju- dices along	
Mr. Peck	weak, no backbone	no details provided	impact of bureaucracy	
Mr. Morrison	strong	large black man	determined and protective; his presence points up the need for protection	
Moe	hard-working	poor	proud and hopeful but really hurt by the system	

Name _____

Attribute Web

Directions: The large center circle is for a character in the book. In the blank smaller circles, fill in verbs. On the lines, supply words to follow each of the verbs; for example, a character might "need love."

Attribute Web for *Shiloh*

Directions: The large center circle is for a character in the book. In the blank smaller circles, fill in verbs. On the lines, supply words to follow each of the verbs; for example, a character might "need love."

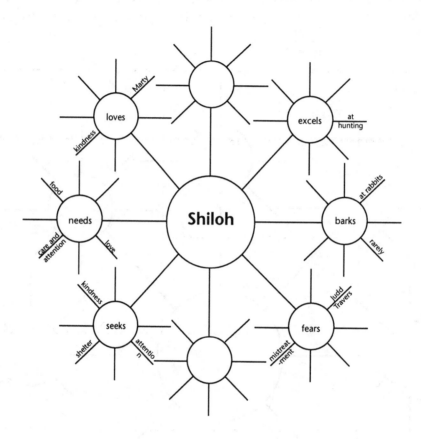

Name _____

Character Chart

Directions: Fill in character names supplied by your teacher across the top boxes. In the boxes across from each of the feelings, describe an incident or time in the book when each character felt that way. You may use "not applicable" if you cannot find an example.

Feeling				
Frustration				
Anger				
Fear				
Humiliation				
Relief				

Character Chart for *Where the Red Fern Grows*

Directions: Fill in character names supplied by your teacher across the top boxes. In the boxes across from each of the feelings, describe an incident or time in the book when each character felt that way. You may use "not applicable" if you cannot find an example.

Feeling	Billy	Papa	Grandpa	
Frustration	*Chapter IX* chopping down the tree and how long it took			
Anger	*Chapter V* gang pulled pup's ears		*Chapter IX* Rainie and Rubin suggest that Billy lied about how good his hounds were	
Fear	*Chapter V* mountain lion stalking Billy and his new dogs			
Humiliation	*Chapter IV* no shoes and country ways; mocked when in town			
Relief		*Chapter VI* when Billy finally returns with pups		
Joy	*Chapter V* accepting delivery of the two hounds			

Teacher Notes

Depending on the particular book, you may ask students to find examples from certain chapters or parts of the book. The graphic can be used to check for compre-hension (reading of a particular chapter <u>while</u> building up a sense of characterization).

To build vocabulary, you may ask students to express frustration, anger, fear, humiliation, and relief in other words. You can adapt the graphic by asking for evidence of other emotions.

Name _____

Characters With Character

Directions: A person's **character** is evaluated by his or her actions, statements, and by the way he or she treats others. For each of the attributes listed in the center of the page, write the name of one character from the novel who has that trait, and the name of a character who does **not** have that trait. After each character's name, give an example of an action or statement which proves you have properly evaluated the character.

Has This Trait		Doesn't Have This Trait
	tells the truth	
	keeps promises	
	considers consequences of actions	
	sacrifices for others	
	listens to others without pre-judging them	
	is a good person	
	is kind and caring	

Characters With Character from *The Golden Goblet*

Directions: A person's **character** is evaluated by his or her actions, statements, and by the way he or she treats others. For each of the attributes listed in the center of the page, write the name of one character from the novel who has that trait, and the name of a character who does **not** have that trait. After each character's name, give an example of an action or statement which proves you have properly evaluated the character.

Has This Trait		Doesn't Have This Trait
	tells the truth	
		Gebu
	keeps promises	
Zau–takes on Ranofer as a pupil after Ranofer reshapes his life.		
	considers consequences of actions	
Ranofer—thinks about effects of taking the golden goblet		
	sacrifices for others	
	listens to others without pre-judging them	
Queen Tiy dwarf		*Guards at palace—don't want to believe Ranofer and let him see the Queen*
	is a good person	
Ranofer		*Gebu—robs graves, involved in smuggling*
	is kind and caring	
		Gebu

Teacher Notes

Characters may be put into multiple boxes as appropriate. Students can be asked for evidence for the placements in the form of actions, statements, and the way he/she treats others.

Name _____

Attribute Web

Directions: Create an attribute web for a character in the book that lists clues about what he/she is like.

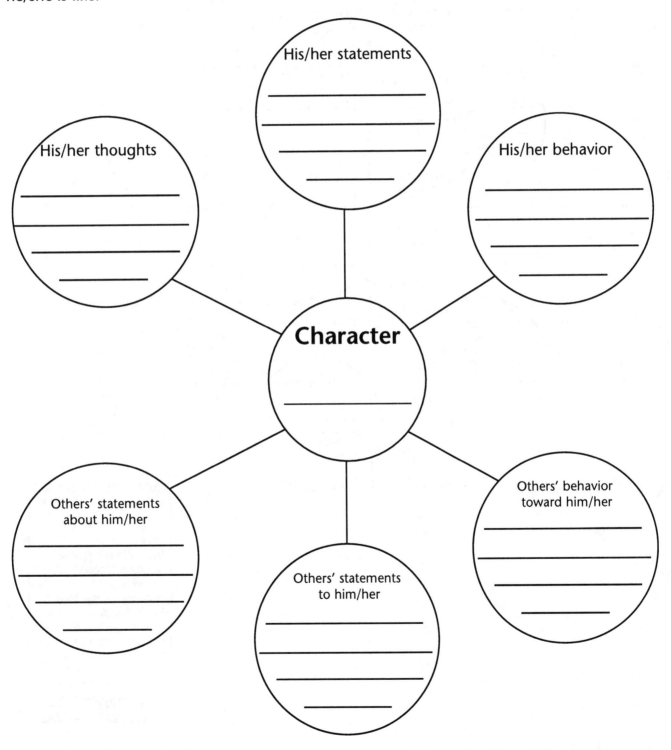

Attribute Web for Scout from *To Kill A Mockingbird*

Directions: Create an attribute web for a character in the book that lists clues about what he/she is like.

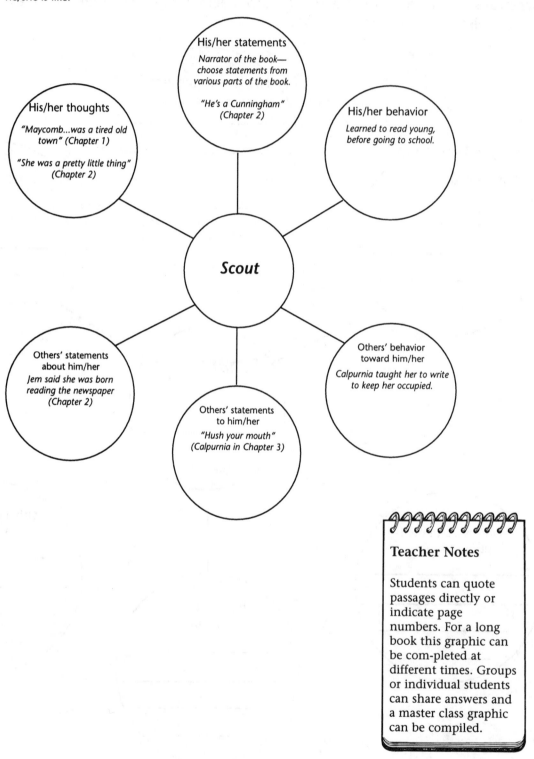

His/her statements

Narrator of the book—choose statements from various parts of the book.

"He's a Cunningham"
(Chapter 2)

His/her thoughts

"Maycomb...was a tired old town" (Chapter 1)

"She was a pretty little thing"
(Chapter 2)

His/her behavior

Learned to read young, before going to school.

Scout

Others' statements about him/her

Jem said she was born reading the newspaper (Chapter 2)

Others' statements to him/her

"Hush your mouth"
(Calpurnia in Chapter 3)

Others' behavior toward him/her

Calpurnia taught her to write to keep her occupied.

Teacher Notes

Students can quote passages directly or indicate page numbers. For a long book this graphic can be com-pleted at different times. Groups or individual students can share answers and a master class graphic can be compiled.

Name _____

Attribute Web

Directions: Create an attribute web for a character in the book. As you read, feel free to add more categories of your own, additional notes, etc.

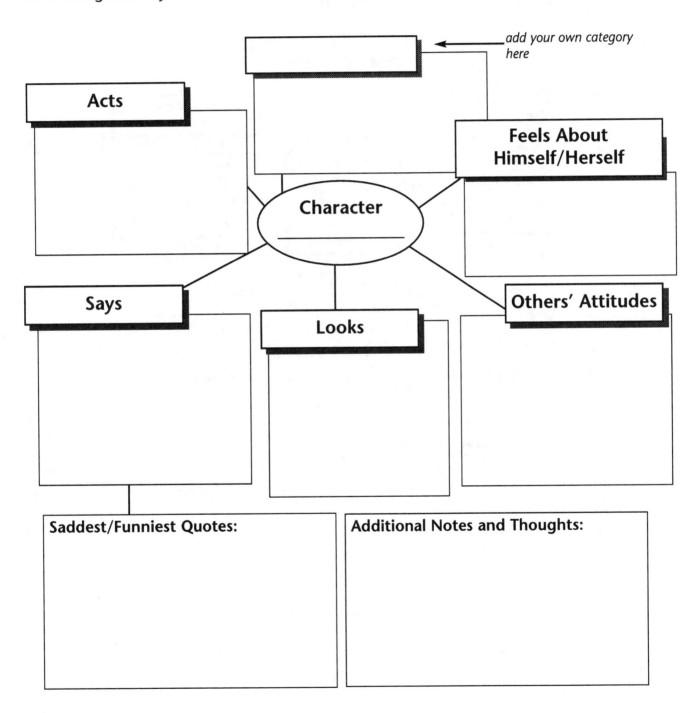

add your own category here

Acts

Feels About Himself/Herself

Character
_____

Says

Looks

Others' Attitudes

Saddest/Funniest Quotes:

Additional Notes and Thoughts:

Attribute Web for Sam Gribley from
My Side of the Mountain

Directions: Create an attribute web for a character in the book. As you read, feel free to add more categories of your own, additional notes, etc.

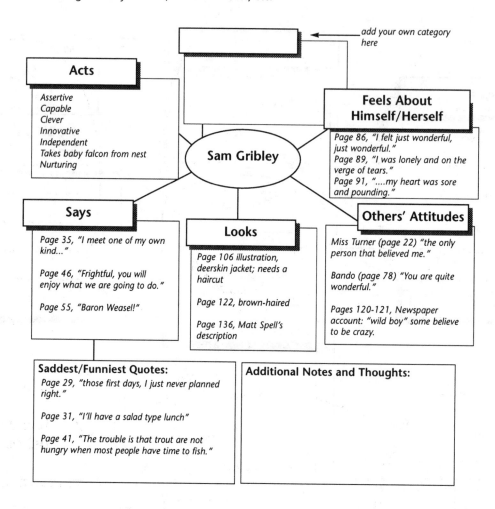

add your own category here

Acts

Assertive
Capable
Clever
Innovative
Independent
Takes baby falcon from nest
Nurturing

Sam Gribley

Feels About Himself/Herself

Page 86, "I felt just wonderful, just wonderful."
Page 89, "I was lonely and on the verge of tears."
Page 91, "....my heart was sore and pounding."

Says

Page 35, "I meet one of my own kind..."

Page 46, "Frightful, you will enjoy what we are going to do."

Page 55, "Baron Weasel!"

Looks

Page 106 illustration, deerskin jacket; needs a haircut

Page 122, brown-haired

Page 136, Matt Spell's description

Others' Attitudes

Miss Turner (page 22) "the only person that believed me."

Bando (page 78) "You are quite wonderful."

Pages 120-121, Newspaper account: "wild boy" some believe to be crazy.

Saddest/Funniest Quotes:
Page 29, "those first days, I just never planned right."

Page 31, "I'll have a salad type lunch"

Page 41, "The trouble is that trout are not hungry when most people have time to fish."

Additional Notes and Thoughts:

Name _____

Attribute Web

Directions: Create an attribute web for a character in the book.

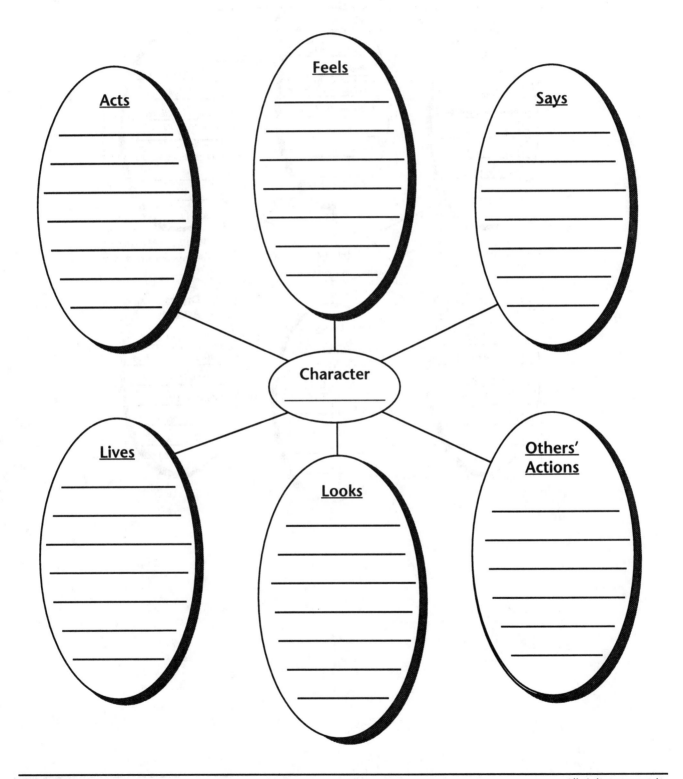

Attribute Web for Jeffrey from *Maniac Magee* Part I

Directions: Create an attribute web for a character in the book.

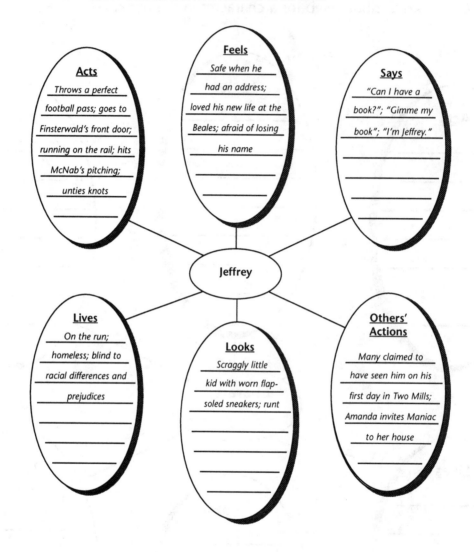

Acts

Throws a perfect football pass; goes to Finsterwald's front door; running on the rail; hits McNab's pitching; unties knots

Feels

Safe when he had an address; loved his new life at the Beales; afraid of losing his name

Says

"Can I have a book?"; "Gimme my book"; "I'm Jeffrey."

Jeffrey

Lives

On the run; homeless; blind to racial differences and prejudices

Looks

Scraggly little kid with worn flap-soled sneakers; runt

Others' Actions

Many claimed to have seen him on his first day in Two Mills; Amanda invites Maniac to her house

Name _____

Attribute Web

Directions: Put the main character's name in the center circle. On the spokes record descriptions. On the smaller spokes beneath each spoke, give examples from the book to support the description.

Attribute Web for Lincoln from

Lincoln: A Photobiography

Directions: Put the main character's name in the center circle. On the spokes record descriptions. On the smaller spokes beneath each spoke, give examples from the book to support the description.

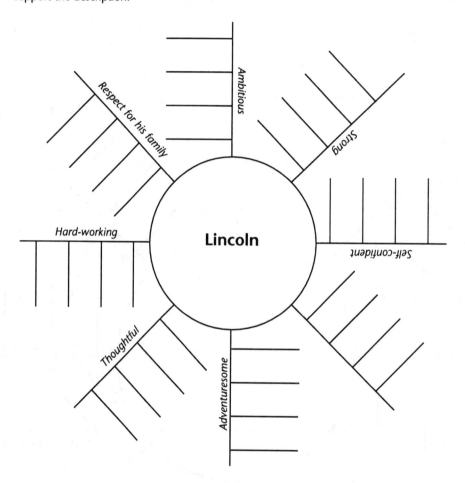

Teacher Notes

Examples from the book can be page numbers or brief quotes. One student can fill in the spoke descriptions and another student can find the evidence.

Name _____

Feelings

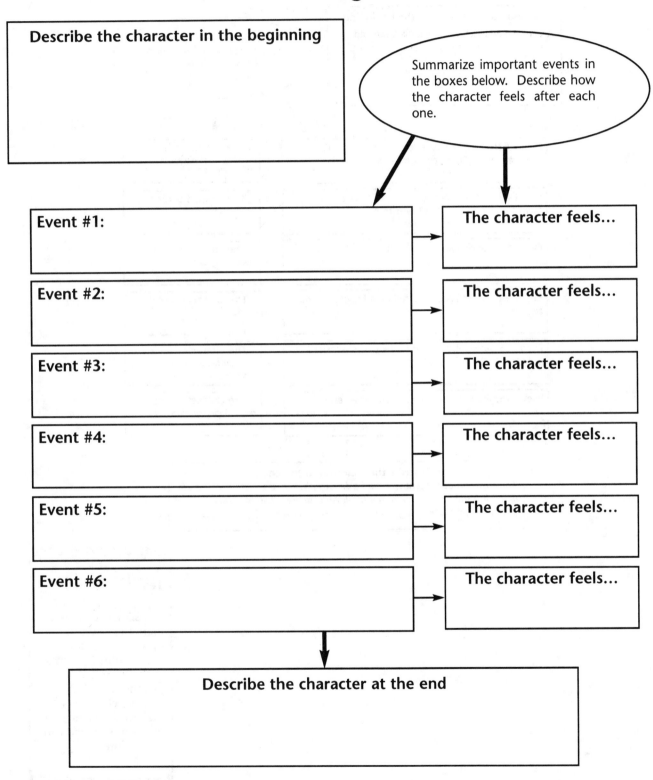

Describe the character in the beginning

Summarize important events in the boxes below. Describe how the character feels after each one.

Event #1:

The character feels…

Event #2:

The character feels…

Event #3:

The character feels…

Event #4:

The character feels…

Event #5:

The character feels…

Event #6:

The character feels…

Describe the character at the end

Feelings for *The Upstairs Room*

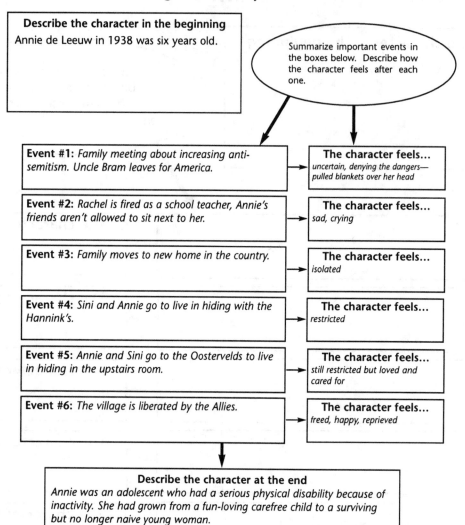

Describe the character in the beginning
Annie de Leeuw in 1938 was six years old.

Summarize important events in the boxes below. Describe how the character feels after each one.

Event #1: *Family meeting about increasing anti-semitism. Uncle Bram leaves for America.*

The character feels...
uncertain, denying the dangers—pulled blankets over her head

Event #2: *Rachel is fired as a school teacher, Annie's friends aren't allowed to sit next to her.*

The character feels...
sad, crying

Event #3: *Family moves to new home in the country.*

The character feels...
isolated

Event #4: *Sini and Annie go to live in hiding with the Hannink's.*

The character feels...
restricted

Event #5: *Annie and Sini go to the Oostervelds to live in hiding in the upstairs room.*

The character feels...
still restricted but loved and cared for

Event #6: *The village is liberated by the Allies.*

The character feels...
freed, happy, reprieved

Describe the character at the end
Annie was an adolescent who had a serious physical disability because of inactivity. She had grown from a fun-loving carefree child to a surviving but no longer naive young woman.

Teacher Notes

The six events noted mark the physical moves in the story. Other kinds of events can be recorded—time periods, introduction of other characters, for example. Evidence for the feelings noted can be requested.

Name _____

Attribute Web

Directions: In the central oval, record a significant event or place or object from the book. Each major character is on the five long lines. The smaller lines, then, are for that particular character's reaction to the significant event, place, or object.

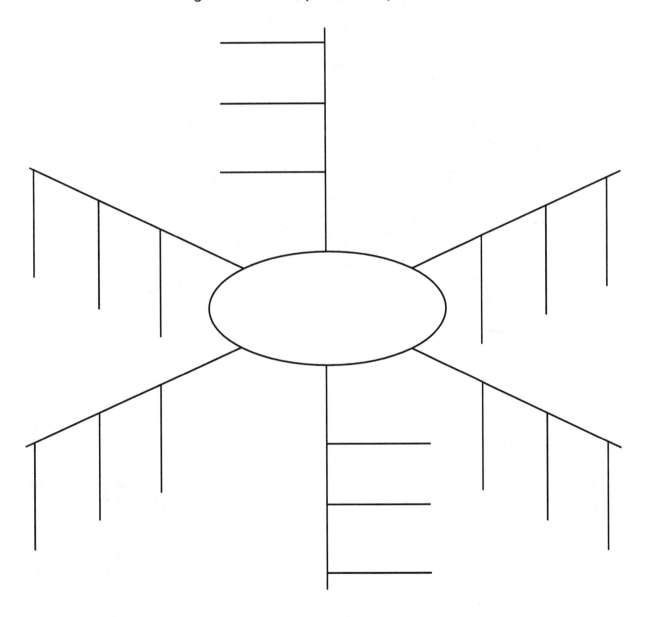

Attribute Web for Sod Dugout from

On the Banks of Plum Creek

Directions: In the central oval, record a significant event or place or object from the book.

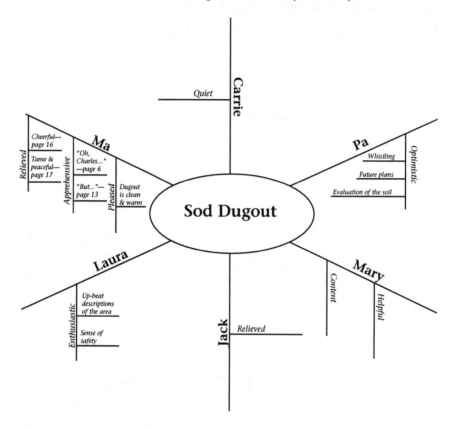

Teacher Notes

This example uses a character web to record ideas about a place. Events, objects, or ideas from the book could also be used as the focus.

Name _____

Character Analysis Chart

Directions: List some of the characters who appear in the novel in the boxes below. Add to this chart as more characters are introduced. Divide the class into groups of four. Discuss the attributes of the various characters with other members of your group. In each character's box, write several words or phrases you feel describe him or her.

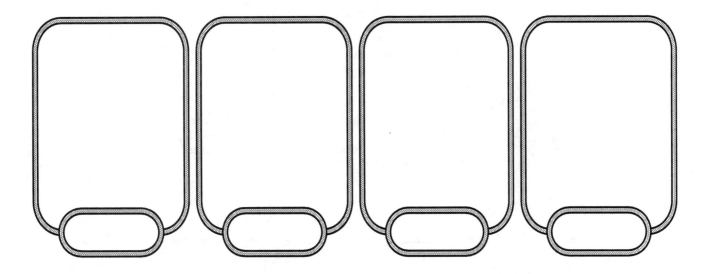

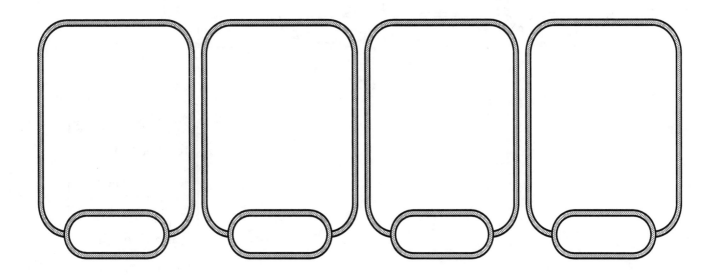

Character Analysis Chart for *The Westing Game*

Directions: List some of the characters who appear in the novel in the boxes below. Add to this chart as more characters are introduced. Divide the class into groups of four. Discuss the attributes of the various characters with other members of your group. In each character's box, write several words or phrases you feel describe him or her.

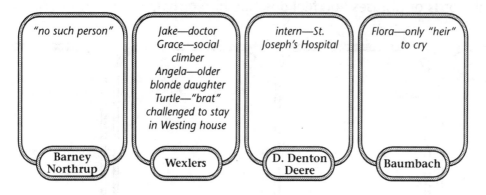

"no such person"

Barney Northrup

Jake—doctor Grace—social climber Angela—older blonde daughter Turtle—"brat" challenged to stay in Westing house

Wexlers

intern—St. Joseph's Hospital

D. Denton Deere

Flora—only "heir" to cry

Baumbach

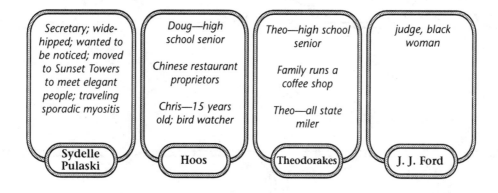

Secretary; wide-hipped; wanted to be noticed; moved to Sunset Towers to meet elegant people; traveling sporadic myositis

Sydelle Pulaski

Doug—high school senior

Chinese restaurant proprietors

Chris—15 years old; bird watcher

Hoos

Theo—high school senior

Family runs a coffee shop

Theo—all state miler

Theodorakes

judge, black woman

J. J. Ford

Teacher Notes

As in the example, this graphic works for mysteries. Each of the characters/sus-pects is assigned a spot for notes. The whole page, then, is like the detective's notebook.

Characterization

Directions: You judge what a character is like in much the same way as you judge what a person in real life is like—by how he/she looks and acts, by what he/she says, by what he/she seems to think and feel, and by how others treat him/her. As you read the story, jot down phrases and page references in the boxes below. For each group of details, write a generalization about the character. Then summarize your generalizations in one or two sentences on the back of your paper.

His/Her Actions	His/Her Thoughts
My generalization:	My generalization:

His/Her Statements	What Others Say to Him/Her
My generalization:	My generalization:

His/Her Feelings	What Others Say About Him/Her
My generalization:	My generalization:

Characterization for Grandpa in

Where the Red Fern Grows

Directions: You judge what a character is like in much the same way as you judge what a person in real life is like—by how he/she looks and acts, by what he/she says, by what he/she seems to think and feel, and by how others treat him/her. As you read the story, jot down phrases and page references in the boxes below. For each group of details, write a generalization about the character. Then summarize your generalizations in one or two sentences on the back of your paper.

His/Her Actions	His/Her Thoughts
Chapter IV—Grandpa helps Billy to finance purchase of the dogs; Chapter IX—Grandpa helps Billy with capturing the treed coon.	*Billy sometimes got a bit excessive in his coon-hunting tales.*
My generalization: *Grandpa has a soft spot in his heart for Billy.*	**My generalization:** *Billy's grandfather understood the bay and knew how to handle him well.*

His/Her Statements:	What Others Say to Him/Her
Chapter IX—heard that there was a New England fad for coonskin caps.	*Chapter XIV—Grandma says he's a baby.*
My generalization: *Encourages Billy indirectly; respects Billy's ability and intelligence.*	**My generalization:** *Grandma likes to nurture Grandpa. She loves him a lot.*

His/Her Feelings	What Others Say About Him/Her
Chapter XII—anger when Rainie and Rubin say they think Billy has lied about his hounds' coon-hunting skill.	*Chapter XIII—"I bet this will break your old grandpa's heart."*
My generalization: *Grandpa is proud of his grandson and is incensed that anyone should criticize Billy.*	**My generalization:** *His support for Billy was unfailing so he'd be really disappointed if Billy failed.*

G
R
A
N
D
P
A

Teacher Notes

You could ask for a couple sentences explaining the true nature of a character. This graphic pro-vides an organization for notes.

Name _____

Sociogram

Directions: On each arrow write the feeling or feelings that the person at the base of the arrow has toward the person to whom the arrow is pointing. (Usually the main character will be in the center oval with the minor characters surrounding it.) Find examples from the text to justify your answers. Write the page number on the line also for your own reference during discussion.

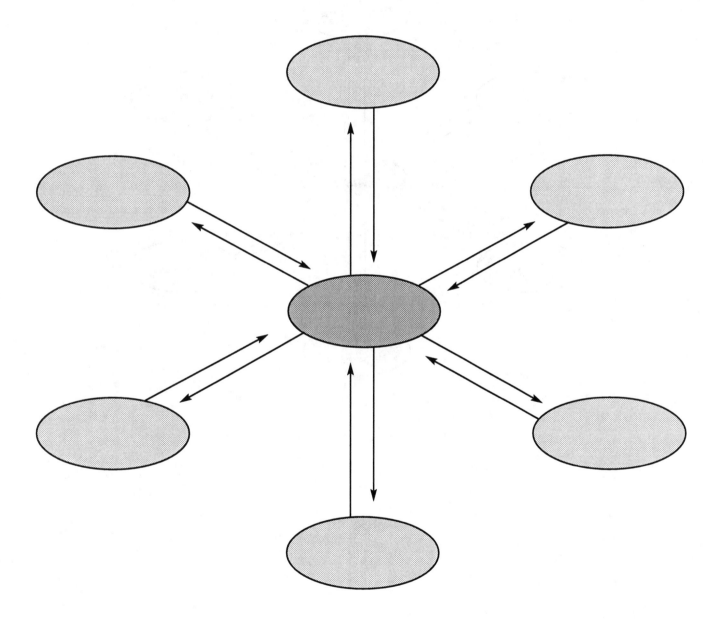

Sociogram for *Little House in the Big Woods*

Directions: On each arrow write the feeling or feelings that the person at the base of the arrow has toward the person to whom the arrow is pointing. (Usually the main character will be in the center oval with the minor characters surrounding it.) Find examples from the text to justify your answers. Write the page number on the line also for your own reference during discussion.

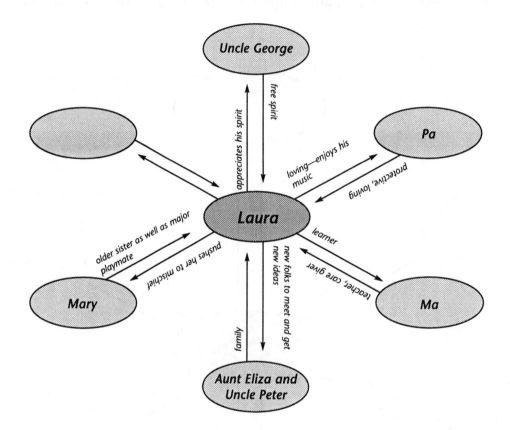

Name _____

Sociogram

Directions: On the "spokes" surrounding each character's name, write several adjectives that describe that character. On the arrows joining one character to another, write a description of the relationship between the two characters. How does one character influence the other?

← —— write adjectives on these lines

Sociogram for *Little House in the Big Woods*

Directions: On the "spokes" surrounding each character's name, write several adjectives that describe that character. On the arrows joining one character to another, write a description of the relationship between the two characters. How does one character influence the other?

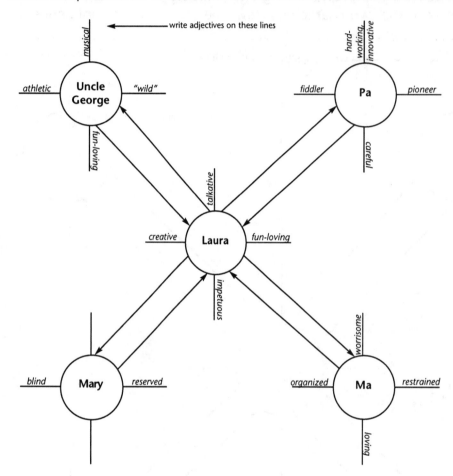

Teacher Notes

Notice how Organizer #18 plays out with adjectives added.

Consider completing the graphics over multiple days or assignments. Different colored pens can be used.

Name _____

Sorting Characters

Directions: Similarities among characters are sometimes a clue to themes in the story. Place the book's characters in one or more of the groups below:

Victims	Victimizers	Fighters
Peace-lovers	**Conformists**	**Self-directors**

61

Sorting Characters for
Cry, the Beloved Country

Directions: Similarities among characters are sometimes a clue to themes in the story. Place the book's characters in one or more of the groups below:

Victims	Victimizers	Fighters
young girl impregnated by Absalom	*Absalom*	*Mr. Carmichael* *Arthur Jarvis's son*
Peace-lovers	**Conformists**	**Self-directors**
Stephen Kumalo *Msimangu* *Arthur Jarvis*	*Mr. Jarvis* *Stephen Kumalo*	*The fighters, peace-lovers, and victimizers might all be considered self-directors.*

Teacher Notes

A follow-up writing exercise would be to define in a single sentence each of the terms: victims, victim- izers, fighters, peace-lovers, conformists, and self-directors.

Name _____

Ensemble Characters

Directions: In the boxes name and identify the book's characters. The center oval is used for a descriptive term for all the characters.

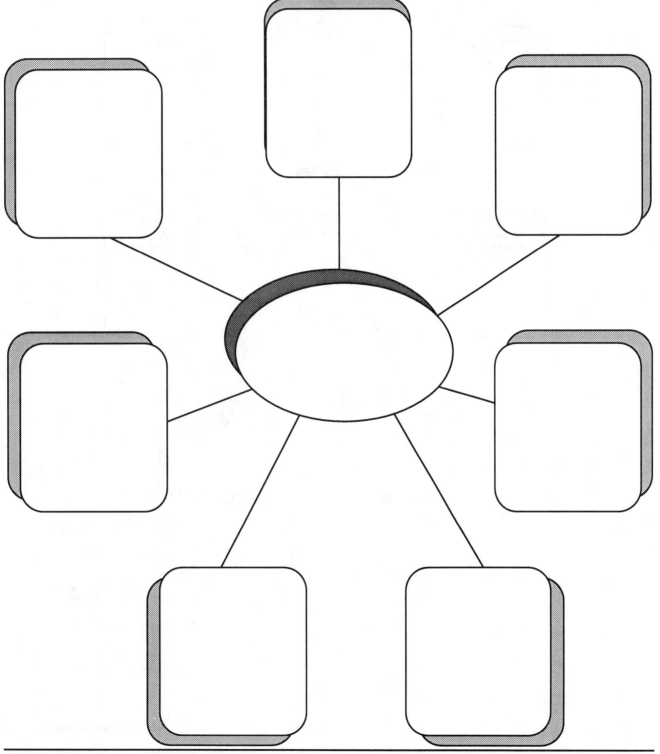

Ensemble Characters for *The House on Mango Street*

Directions: In the boxes name and identify the book's characters. The center oval is used for a descriptive term for all the characters.

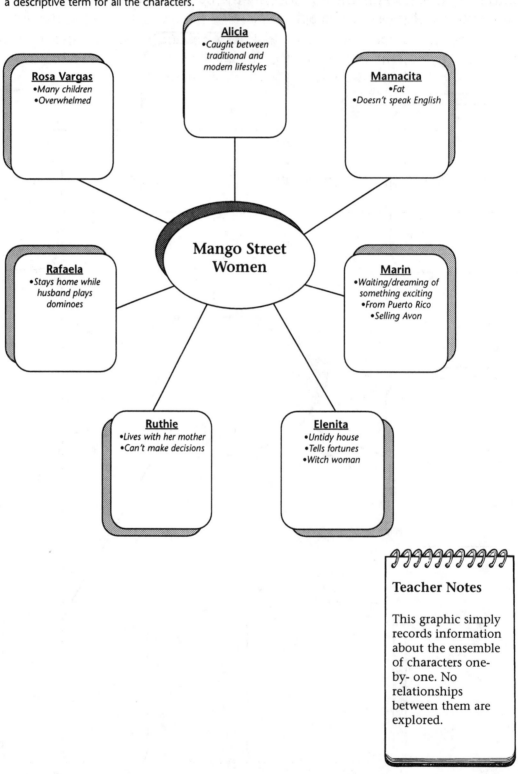

Alicia
•Caught between traditional and modern lifestyles

Rosa Vargas
•Many children
•Overwhelmed

Mamacita
•Fat
•Doesn't speak English

Mango Street Women

Rafaela
•Stays home while husband plays dominoes

Marin
•Waiting/dreaming of something exciting
•From Puerto Rico
•Selling Avon

Ruthie
•Lives with her mother
•Can't make decisions

Elenita
•Untidy house
•Tells fortunes
•Witch woman

Teacher Notes

This graphic simply records information about the ensemble of characters one-by- one. No relationships between them are explored.

Name _____

Characterization

Directions: Characterization is the portrayal of an imaginary person by what he says or does, by what others say about him or how they react to him, and by what the author reveals directly or through a narrator. As you read, look for clues to what a specific character is like. Think about why he/she and others act and speak as they do—and what traits these actions and words reveal. Fill in the chart below to record your ideas.

Character:			
Action/Words	**Reason**	**Trait**	**Narrator's Comments**

© Novel Units, Inc.

65

Characterization for *Ethan Fromme*

Directions: Characterization is the portrayal of an imaginary person by what he says or does, by what others say about him or how they react to him, and by what the author reveals directly or through a narrator. As you read, look for clues to what a specific character is like. Think about why he/she and others act and speak as they do—and what traits these actions and words reveal. Fill in the chart below to record your ideas.

Character: Ethan Fromme			
Action/Words	**Reason**	**Trait**	**Narrator's Comments**
Ethan tells Mattie about the stars.	He enjoys her sense of wonder.	sensitivity	"He had always been more sensitive than the people about him to the appeal of natural beauty." (page 25)

Name _____

Characterization

Directions: Place words that describe the character in the center oval in the bubbles around his name. Place details from the story that demonstrate each quality in the rectangles.

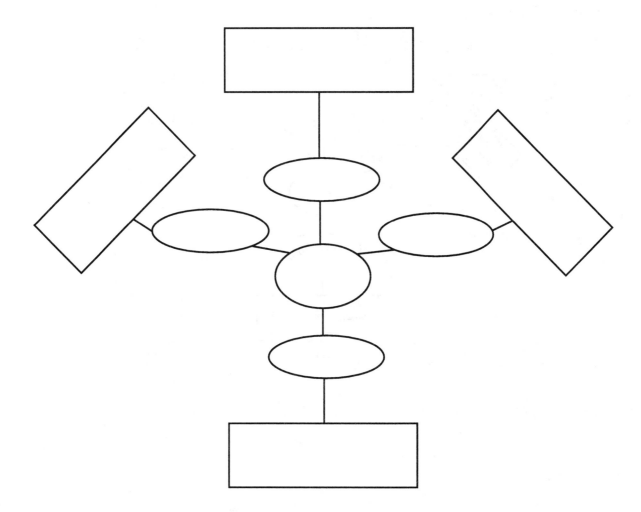

Characterization for Tony from

On My Honor

Directions: Place words that describe the character in the center oval in the bubbles around his name. Place details from the story that demonstrate each quality in the rectangles.

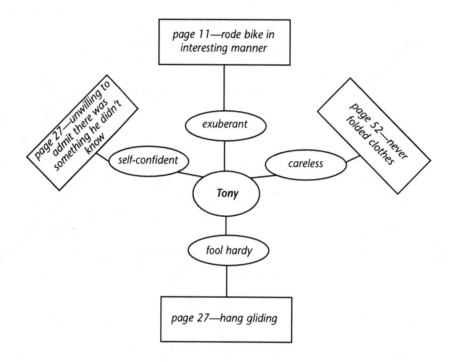

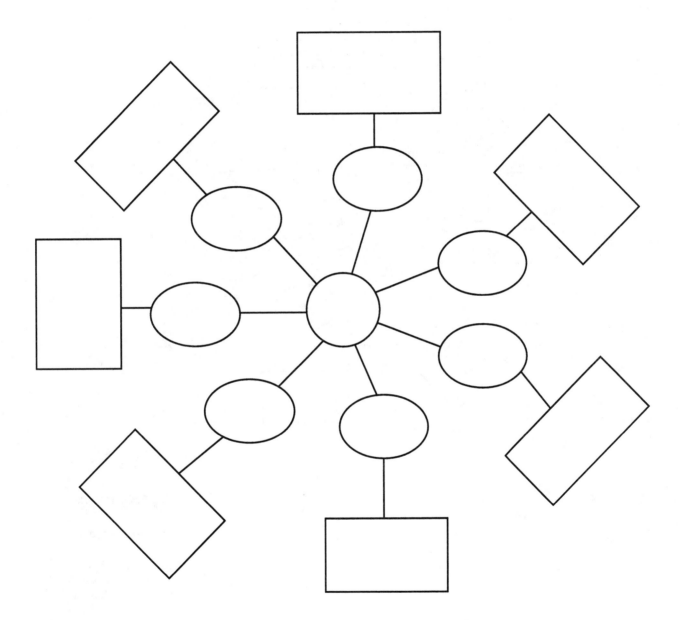

Name _____

Characterization

Directions: Write a word or phrase describing the character in each oval. Describe a behavior (action demonstrating that trait) in each rectangle.

Characterization for Henry from

The Red Badge of Courage

Directions: Write a word or phrase describing the character in each oval. Describe a behavior (action demonstrating that trait) in each rectangle.

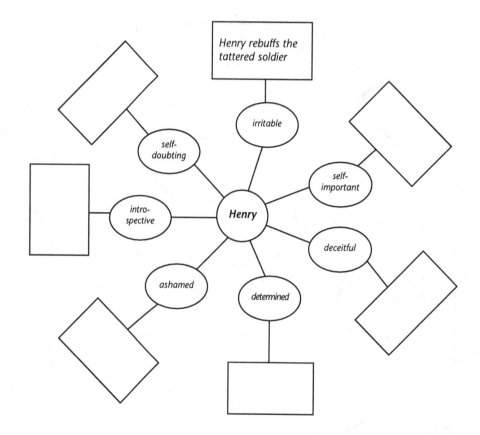

© Novel Units, Inc.

Name _____

Characterization

Directions: Place in each oval an adjective that describes the character in the center of the page. Fill in each rectangle with a detail that illustrates the quality in the oval.

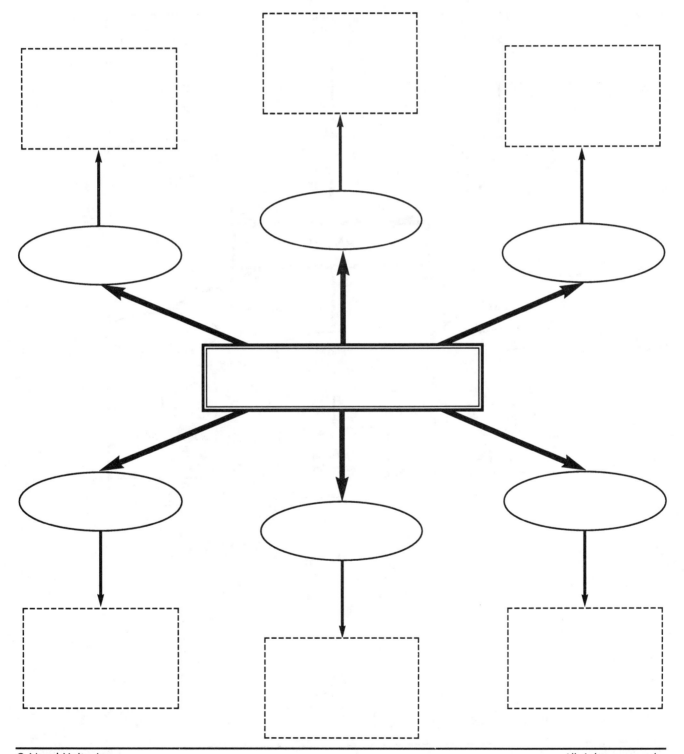

Characterization for Angel from *Tess of the D'Urbervilles*

Directions: Place in each oval an adjective that describes the character in the center of the page. Fill in each rectangle with a detail that illustrates the quality in the oval.

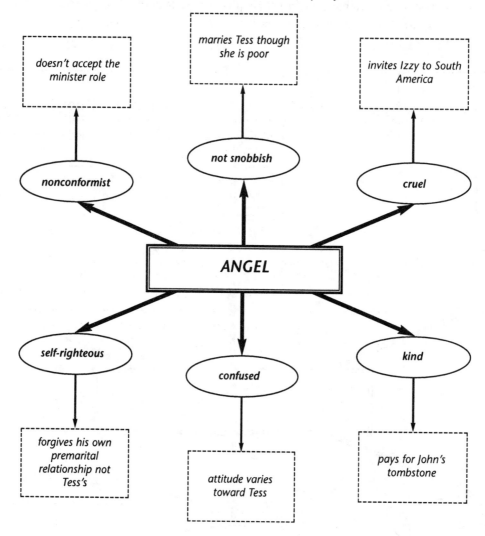

Story Maps

Story maps provide a systematic way to review the elements of a story. They may be used as a predicting tool to foretell a story, as a story is read to reveal story elements, or as a summary to recall a story's development and resolution. In a classroom teaching setting, story maps can be completed together as a group, in cooperative groups, or individually.

Story Map Element	Question Prompt	Extension Questions
Setting	Where? When?	Why is this an intriguing setting? How does the setting support the story?
Characters	Who?	Who is the protagonist? Who are the main characters? the supporting characters? What is the point of view of the book?
Problem	Did what? Why?	What is the goal of the story? What questions does the plot present?
Solution/ Resolution	How did it end?	What is the climax of the story? the conclusion? Is there falling action? How does the author round out the ending?

Students can use blank "charts" to fill in story maps or they can be challenged to devise their own maps. The blank frameworks vary, but usually include some form of the above story map elements.

An intriguing "Bare Bones Story Map" is simply, <u>Somebody</u> / <u>wanted</u> / <u>but</u> / <u>so</u>.

Types of plot lines:

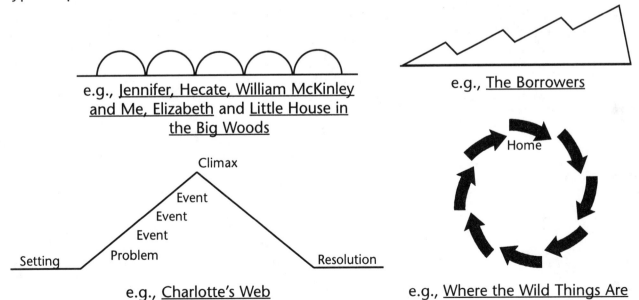

e.g., <u>Jennifer, Hecate, William McKinley and Me, Elizabeth</u> and <u>Little House in the Big Woods</u>

e.g., <u>The Borrowers</u>

e.g., <u>Charlotte's Web</u>

e.g., <u>Where the Wild Things Are</u>

Writing Assignments to be Used with Story Maps

- Which element of the story is emphasized in this particular work?

- What elements are typically emphasized in certain genres?
  mysteries
  fantasy
  biography
  quest

- Why is this graphic a good fit for this book?

- Use one word to trigger answers for:
  setting;
  exposition;
  conflict;
  climax;
  denouement.

Name _____

Story Map

Directions: Complete the story map below. Work in small groups. (The map could be completed following reading of the entire story, or after each assigned section is read.)

Settings/Main Characters
Statement of the Problem

Event 1

Event 2

Event 3

Event 4

Event 5

Statement of the Solution

Story Theme (what is the author really trying to tell us about people in general?)

Story Map for *The Phantom Tollbooth*

by Norton Juster

Directions: Complete the story map below. Work in small groups. (The map could be completed following reading of the entire story, or after each assigned section is read.)

Settings/Main Characters: *Expectations, Doldrums, Dictionopolis, Milo, Watchdog, Humbug*

Statement of the Problem: *Milo has an adventure via the phantom tollbooth. He makes sense of his own world and what is important to him allegorically by means of his adventures. There is a quest adventure to secure the release of two captive princesses.*

Event 1: *Milo assembles the tollbooth, chooses Dictionopolis as his destination and drives off.*

Event 2: *Milo and his companion Tock meet Humbug as well as the many fanciful characters in Dictionopolis.*

Event 3: *Milo hears about the imprisoned princesses, Rhyme and Reason, and sets out to rescue them.*

Event 4: *The trio travel through Illusions and Reality, the Silent Valley, Unfortunate Conclusions, Digitopolis, Infinity, Ignorance.*

Event 5: *Milo arrives at the Castle in the Air and rescues the princesses.*

Statement of the Solution: *The princesses (Rhyme and Reason) are rescued. In the process, Milo meets several interesting characters who, allegorically, present some important ideas.*

Story Theme (what is the author really trying to tell us about people in general?): *Words can be fun friends. Allegory is a way to make sense of the world.*

Name _____

Story Map

Directions: Discuss the problem the characters faced, and the solution they developed, by completing the following problem-solving frame.

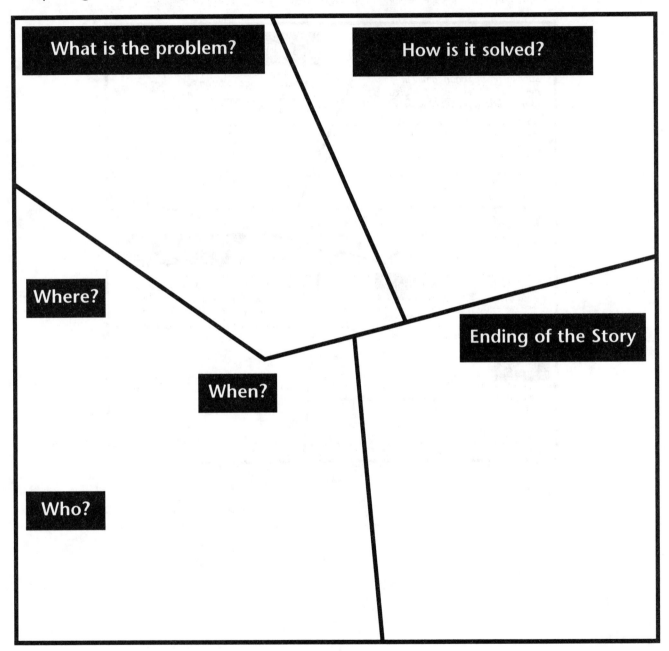

Story Map for *Roll of Thunder, Hear My Cry*
by Mildred Taylor

Directions: Discuss the problem the characters faced, and the solution they developed, by completing the following problem-solving frame.

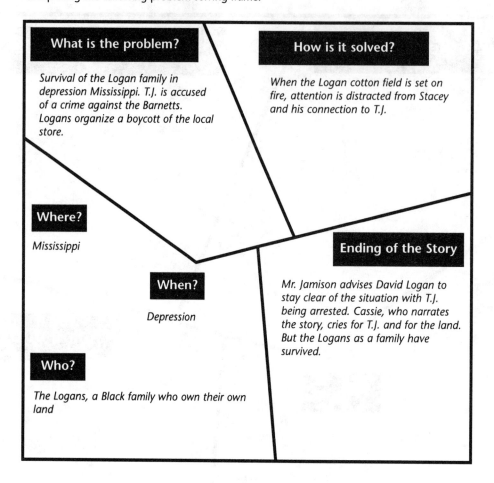

What is the problem?

Survival of the Logan family in depression Mississippi. T.J. is accused of a crime against the Barnetts. Logans organize a boycott of the local store.

How is it solved?

When the Logan cotton field is set on fire, attention is distracted from Stacey and his connection to T.J.

Where?

Mississippi

When?

Depression

Ending of the Story

Mr. Jamison advises David Logan to stay clear of the situation with T.J. being arrested. Cassie, who narrates the story, cries for T.J. and for the land. But the Logans as a family have survived.

Who?

The Logans, a Black family who own their own land

Name _____

Story Map

Directions: Use the diagram below with a partner or small group to free-associate thoughts about the novel after you have finished reading it. Jot down your thoughts in a similar format on a large piece of paper.

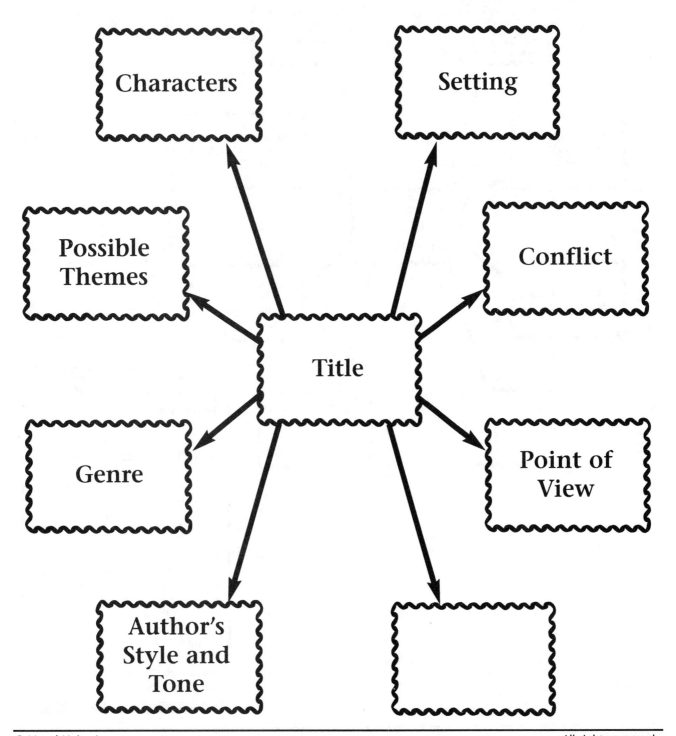

79

Story Map for *Across Five Aprils* by Irene Hunt

Directions: Use the diagram below with a partner or small group to free-associate thoughts about the novel after you have finished reading it. Jot down your thoughts in a similar format on a large piece of paper.

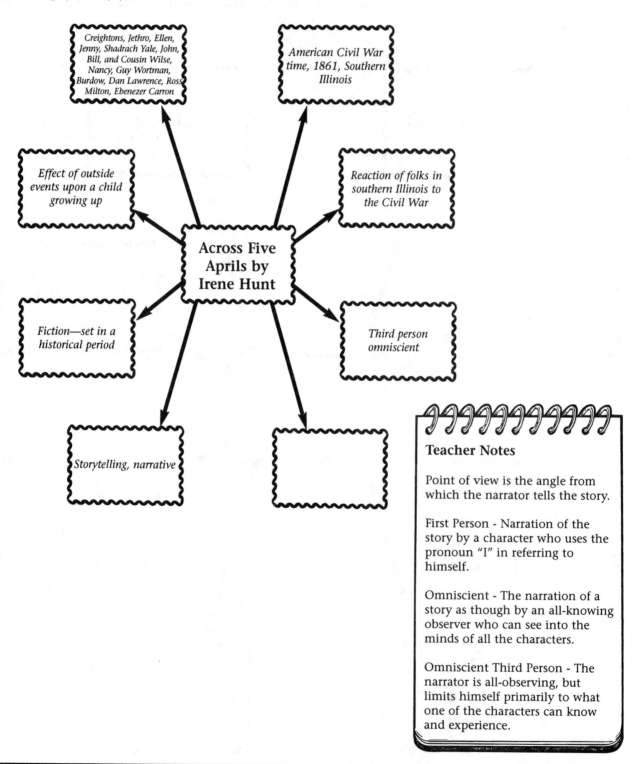

Creightons, Jethro, Ellen, Jenny, Shadrach Yale, John, Bill, and Cousin Wilse, Nancy, Guy Wortman, Burdow, Dan Lawrence, Ross Milton, Ebenezer Carron

American Civil War time, 1861, Southern Illinois

Effect of outside events upon a child growing up

Reaction of folks in southern Illinois to the Civil War

Across Five Aprils by Irene Hunt

Fiction—set in a historical period

Third person omniscient

Storytelling, narrative

Teacher Notes

Point of view is the angle from which the narrator tells the story.

First Person - Narration of the story by a character who uses the pronoun "I" in referring to himself.

Omniscient - The narration of a story as though by an all-knowing observer who can see into the minds of all the characters.

Omniscient Third Person - The narrator is all-observing, but limits himself primarily to what one of the characters can know and experience.

Name _____

Story Map

Directions: Fill in each box below with information about the novel.

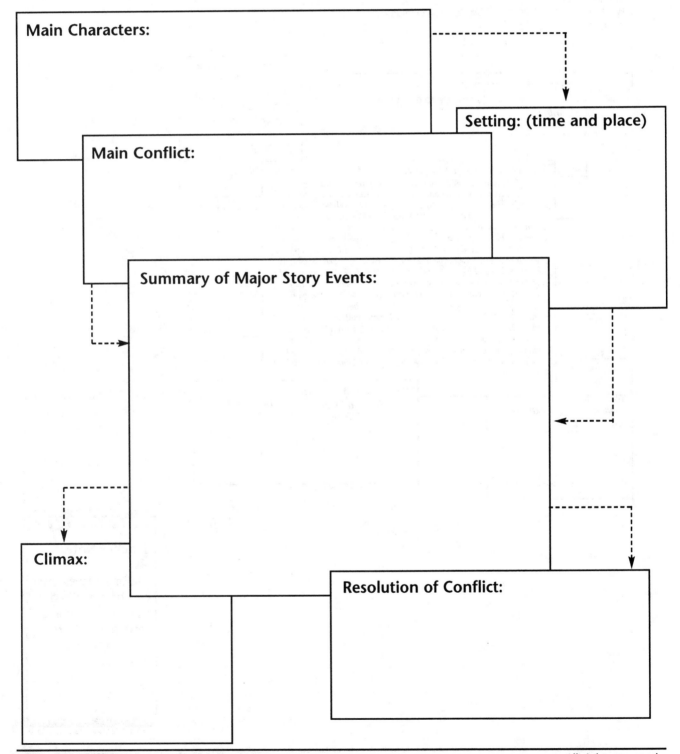

Main Characters:

Setting: (time and place)

Main Conflict:

Summary of Major Story Events:

Climax:

Resolution of Conflict:

Story Map for *The White Mountains* by John Christopher

Directions: Fill in each box below with information about the novel.

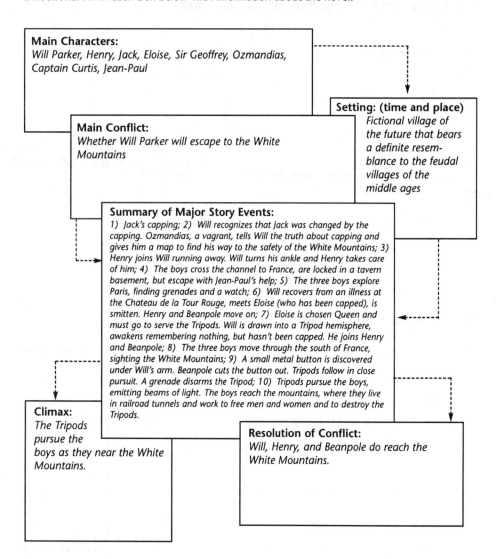

Main Characters:
Will Parker, Henry, Jack, Eloise, Sir Geoffrey, Ozmandias, Captain Curtis, Jean-Paul

Setting: (time and place)
Fictional village of the future that bears a definite resemblance to the feudal villages of the middle ages

Main Conflict:
Whether Will Parker will escape to the White Mountains

Summary of Major Story Events:
1) Jack's capping; 2) Will recognizes that Jack was changed by the capping. Ozmandias, a vagrant, tells Will the truth about capping and gives him a map to find his way to the safety of the White Mountains; 3) Henry joins Will running away. Will turns his ankle and Henry takes care of him; 4) The boys cross the channel to France, are locked in a tavern basement, but escape with Jean-Paul's help; 5) The three boys explore Paris, finding grenades and a watch; 6) Will recovers from an illness at the Chateau de la Tour Rouge, meets Eloise (who has been capped), is smitten. Henry and Beanpole move on; 7) Eloise is chosen Queen and must go to serve the Tripods. Will is drawn into a Tripod hemisphere, awakens remembering nothing, but hasn't been capped. He joins Henry and Beanpole; 8) The three boys move through the south of France, sighting the White Mountains; 9) A small metal button is discovered under Will's arm. Beanpole cuts the button out. Tripods follow in close pursuit. A grenade disarms the Tripod; 10) Tripods pursue the boys, emitting beams of light. The boys reach the mountains, where they live in railroad tunnels and work to free men and women and to destroy the Tripods.

Climax:
The Tripods pursue the boys as they near the White Mountains.

Resolution of Conflict:
Will, Henry, and Beanpole do reach the White Mountains.

Teacher Notes

Major story events can be described in comprehensive sentences, short paragraphs, or phrases.

Name _____

Episodic Story Map

Directions: Fill in the characters, setting (time and place), problem, and solution in the first box. The flow chart boxes below are for the various episodes in the story.

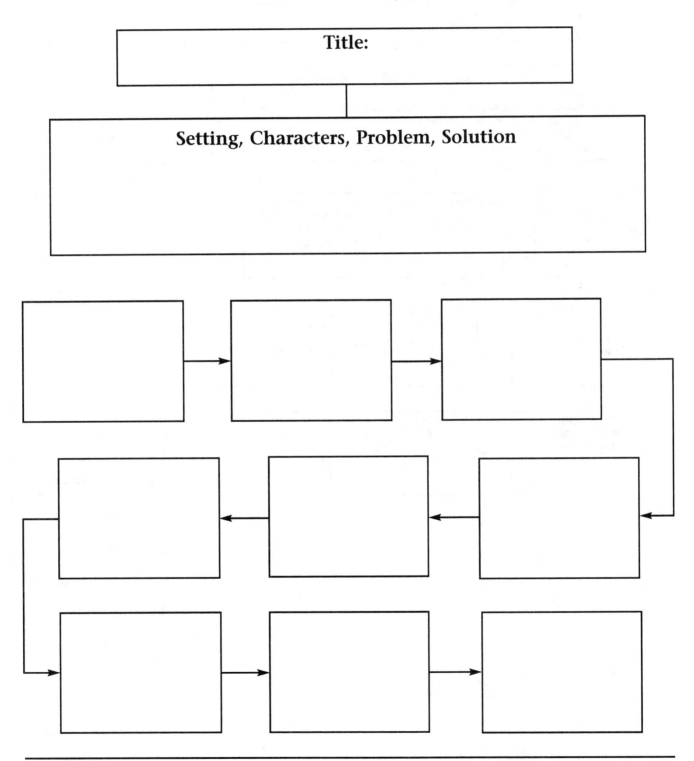

Title:

Setting, Characters, Problem, Solution

Episodic Story Map for *Miss Rumphius* by Barbara Cooney

Directions: Fill in the characters, setting (time and place), problem, and solution in the first box. The flow chart boxes below are for the various episodes in the story.

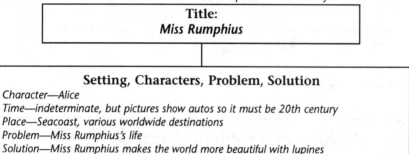

Title:
Miss Rumphius

Setting, Characters, Problem, Solution
Character—Alice
Time—indeterminate, but pictures show autos so it must be 20th century
Place—Seacoast, various worldwide destinations
Problem—Miss Rumphius's life
Solution—Miss Rumphius makes the world more beautiful with lupines

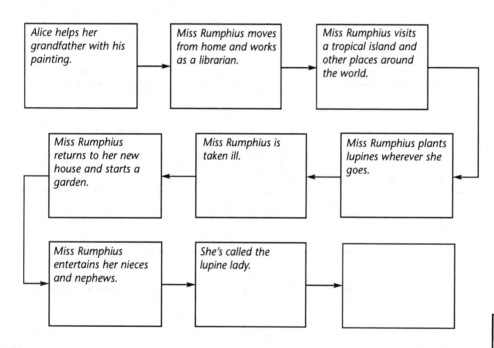

Alice helps her grandfather with his painting.

Miss Rumphius moves from home and works as a librarian.

Miss Rumphius visits a tropical island and other places around the world.

Miss Rumphius returns to her new house and starts a garden.

Miss Rumphius is taken ill.

Miss Rumphius plants lupines wherever she goes.

Miss Rumphius entertains her nieces and nephews.

She's called the lupine lady.

Teacher Notes

For biographies or other episodic stories, the flow chart story map works well. Students can answer with narrative sentences or phrases or a simple line drawing.

Name _____

Literal Story Map

Directions: Construct a literal story map of the story which summarizes it visually. The theme is indicated in the center. Chronologically list main events or settings around the theme bubble. Characters, events, actions, consequences, and reactions are attached chronologically around the setting/event bubbles. Add bubbles if you wish.

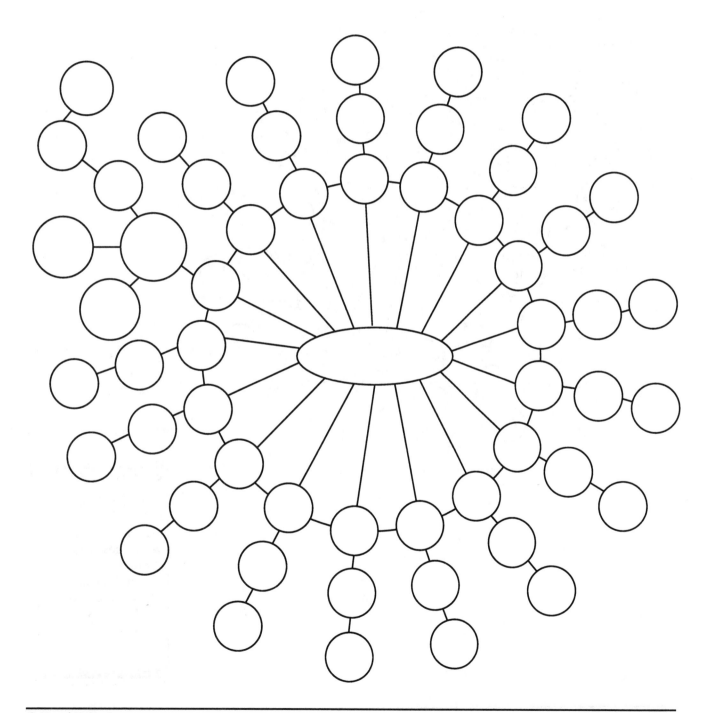

85

Literal Story Map for *Woodsong* by Gary Paulsen

Directions: Construct a literal story map of the story which summarizes it visually. The theme is indicated in the center. Chronologically list main events or settings around the theme bubble. Characters, events, actions, consequences, and reactions are attached chronologically around the setting/event bubbles. Add bubbles if you wish.

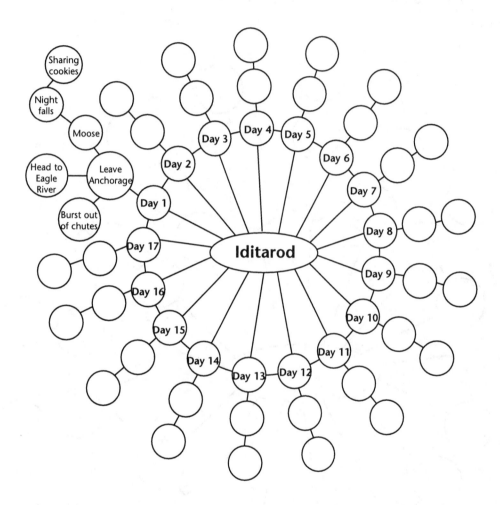

Name _____

SETTING...CHARACTERS...ACTION!

Directions: Answer the questions in a short sentence or two. Fill in setting and character boxes.

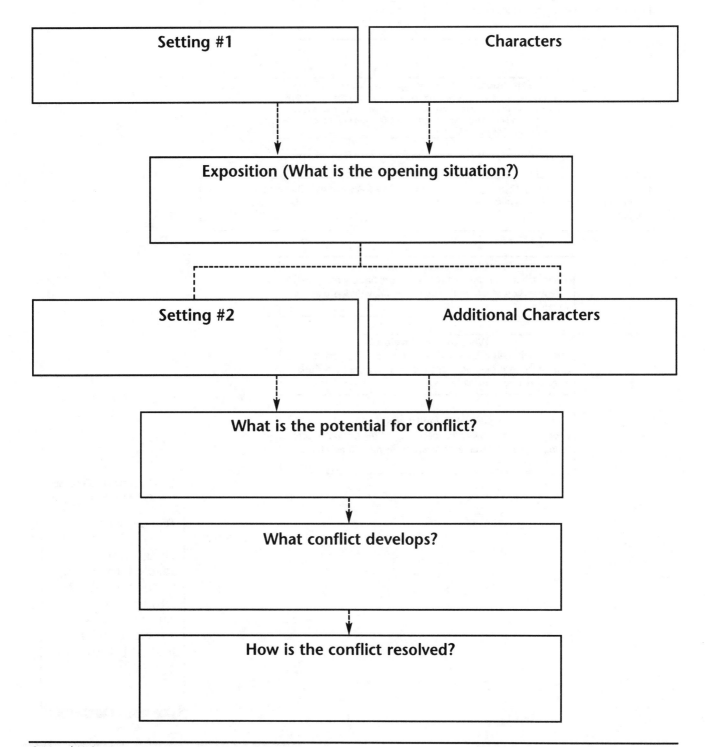

SETTING...CHARACTERS...ACTION! FOR *OF MICE AND MEN* BY JOHN STEINBECK

Directions: Answer the questions in a short sentence or two. Fill in setting and character boxes.

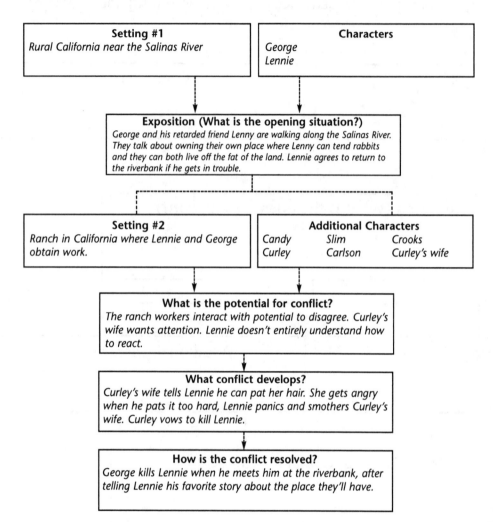

Setting #1
Rural California near the Salinas River

Characters
George
Lennie

Exposition (What is the opening situation?)
George and his retarded friend Lenny are walking along the Salinas River. They talk about owning their own place where Lenny can tend rabbits and they can both live off the fat of the land. Lennie agrees to return to the riverbank if he gets in trouble.

Setting #2
Ranch in California where Lennie and George obtain work.

Additional Characters
Candy   Slim   Crooks
Curley   Carlson   Curley's wife

What is the potential for conflict?
The ranch workers interact with potential to disagree. Curley's wife wants attention. Lennie doesn't entirely understand how to react.

What conflict develops?
Curley's wife tells Lennie he can pat her hair. She gets angry when he pats it too hard, Lennie panics and smothers Curley's wife. Curley vows to kill Lennie.

How is the conflict resolved?
George kills Lennie when he meets him at the riverbank, after telling Lennie his favorite story about the place they'll have.

Teacher Notes

The graphic can be adapted depending on the number of settings in a particular book. The questions direct student investigation.

Name _____

Story Map

Directions: Select five important happenings from the story to put into this flow chart. Be sure to choose carefully so that you'll cover the plot in the book through the last chapter.

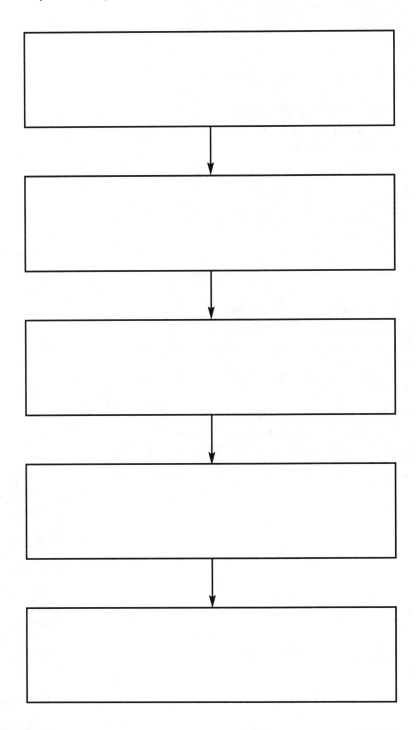

Story Map for *Number the Stars* by Lois Lowry

Directions: Select five important happenings from the story to put into this flow chart. Be sure to choose carefully so that you'll cover the plot in the book through the last chapter.

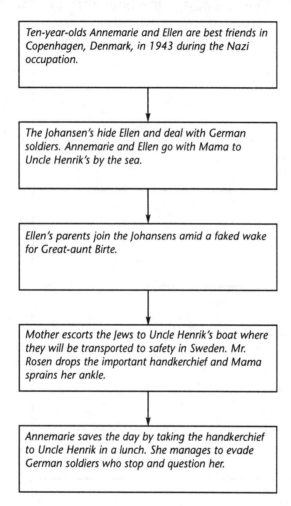

Ten-year-olds Annemarie and Ellen are best friends in Copenhagen, Denmark, in 1943 during the Nazi occupation.

The Johansen's hide Ellen and deal with German soldiers. Annemarie and Ellen go with Mama to Uncle Henrik's by the sea.

Ellen's parents join the Johansens amid a faked wake for Great-aunt Birte.

Mother escorts the Jews to Uncle Henrik's boat where they will be transported to safety in Sweden. Mr. Rosen drops the important handkerchief and Mama sprains her ankle.

Annemarie saves the day by taking the handkerchief to Uncle Henrik in a lunch. She manages to evade German soldiers who stop and question her.

Teacher Notes

With this graphic, we ask students to synthe-size and evaluate, choosing the five most significant events of the story. The sample answers are given narratively. Simple line drawings are another alternative way to answer.

Name _____

Create a Word Map For One of the Book's Themes

Directions: Choose a theme from the book to be the focus of your word map. Complete a web and then fill in the stars.

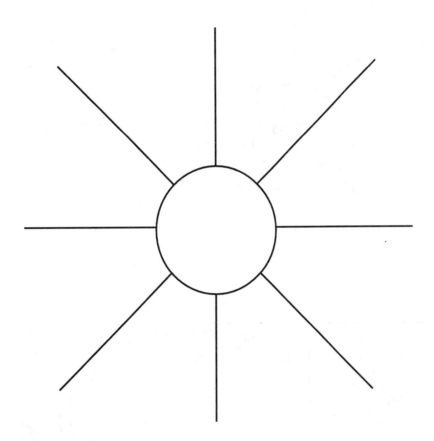

 What is the author's main message?

 What did you learn from the book?

91

Create a Word Map For One of the Book's Themes

for *Number the Stars* by Lois Lowry

Directions: Choose a theme from the book to be the focus of your word map. Complete a web and then fill in the stars.

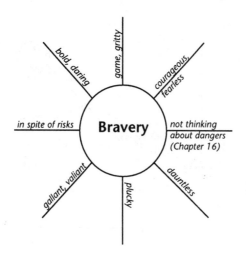

game, gritty
bold, daring
courageous, fearless
in spite of risks
Bravery
not thinking about dangers (Chapter 16)
gallant, valiant
plucky
dauntless

 What is the author's main message?

Bravery is knowing what you need to do, staying focused, and overcoming your fears. Bravery has no gender or age restrictions.

 What did you learn from the book?

Teacher Notes

Several of the web responses on the suggested answers are synonyms for brave. Students could also suggest book characters, quotes, and others from their own experience or reading.

The second star responses will vary, but do need to refer directly to the theme chosen for the web.

Name _____

Story Map

Directions: Record the setting, characters, and problem first. Then follow the arrow to the plot line to record the increasing conflict and incidents leading to the climax. Note the turning point and resolution.

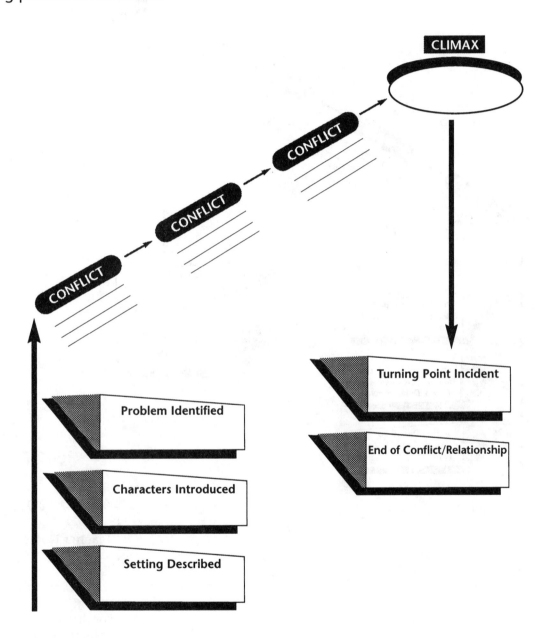

Story Map for *Shiloh* by Phyllis Reynolds Naylor

Directions: Record the setting, characters, and problem first. Then follow the arrow to the plot line to record the increasing conflict and incidents leading to the climax. Note the turning point and resolution.

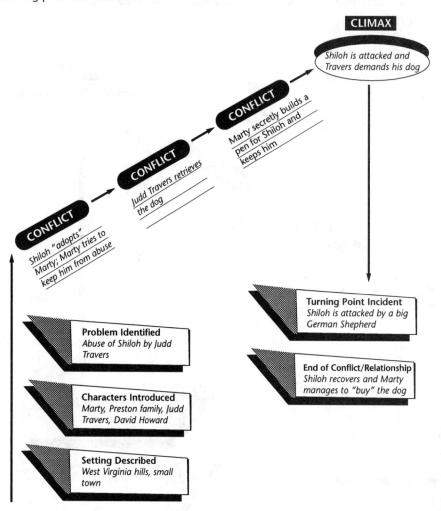

CLIMAX

Shiloh is attacked and Travers demands his dog

CONFLICT

Marty secretly builds a pen for Shiloh and keeps him

CONFLICT

Judd Travers retrieves the dog

CONFLICT

Shiloh "adopts" Marty; Marty tries to keep him from abuse

Problem Identified
Abuse of Shiloh by Judd Travers

Characters Introduced
Marty, Preston family, Judd Travers, David Howard

Setting Described
West Virginia hills, small town

Turning Point Incident
Shiloh is attacked by a big German Shepherd

End of Conflict/Relationship
Shiloh recovers and Marty manages to "buy" the dog

Teacher Notes

This story map works best with a plot of increasing conflict with a dramatic climax and then denouement to resolve the conflicts.

Name _____

Novel Web Diagram

Directions: The oval is the place for the book's title. Then fill in the boxes to summarize the story.

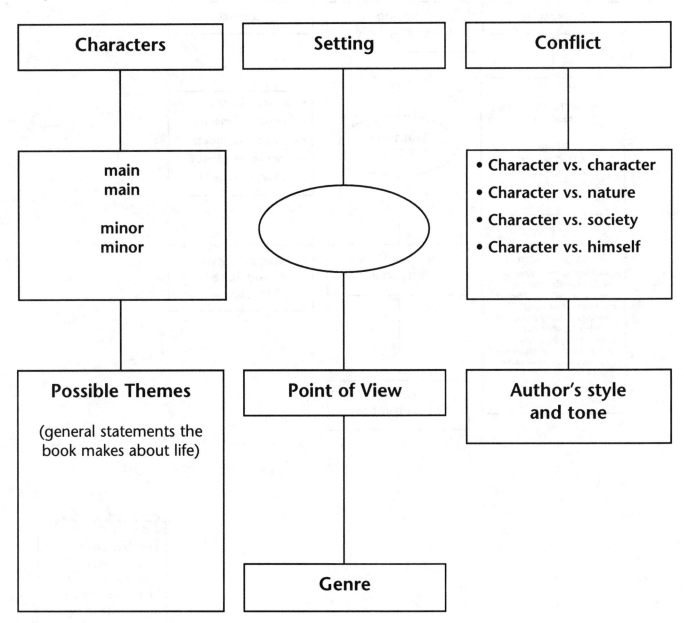

Novel Web Diagram for *Transport 7-41-R* by T. Degens

Directions: The oval is the place for the book's title. Then fill in the boxes to summarize the story.

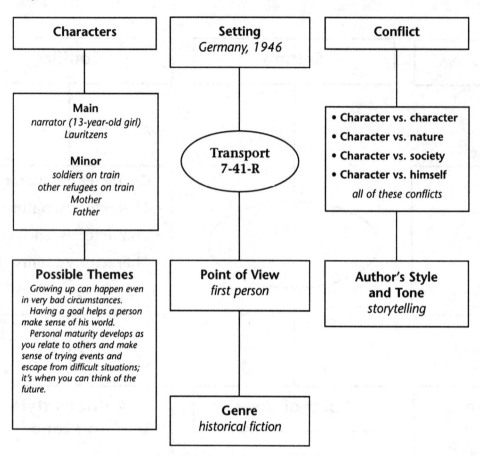

Characters

Main
narrator (13-year-old girl)
Lauritzens

Minor
soldiers on train
other refugees on train
Mother
Father

Possible Themes
Growing up can happen even in very bad circumstances.
Having a goal helps a person make sense of his world.
Personal maturity develops as you relate to others and make sense of trying events and escape from difficult situations; it's when you can think of the future.

Setting
Germany, 1946

Transport 7-41-R

Point of View
first person

Genre
historical fiction

Conflict

- **Character vs. character**
- **Character vs. nature**
- **Character vs. society**
- **Character vs. himself**
all of these conflicts

Author's Style and Tone
storytelling

Teacher Notes

The graphic can be converted to an overhead or large poster to direct student discussion. Examples of the kinds of conflict can be elicited.

Comprehension Strategies

Comprehension is an active process in which readers interpret what they read in accordance with what is already known about the topic. It is an active learning process in which students integrate prior knowledge with text information to create new knowledge. To maximize reading comprehension, teachers need to find ways to help students activate and retrieve prior knowledge related to the topic about which they will be reading. Students need ways to organize, to visualize what they are learning. Graphic organizers provide the tools to improve comprehension.

There are four levels of comprehension—literal meaning, interpretive reading, critical evaluation, and synthesis reading. The first level or base level is literal meaning. **Literal meaning** level calls for the ability to identify the author's words and to understand their meanings in context. On the second level, **interpretive reading**, the reader is able to go beyond an author's words by inferring what they imply. Comprehension requires readers to use what they know that is relevant in order to add more to the message than an author's words communicate. In the third level, **critical comprehension**, the reader evaluates the material judging the worth, validity, or authenticity of the material. The reader judges the accuracy of the ideas. In **synthesis reading**, the fourth level, the reader integrates ideas in the text with his own ideas to develop new insights or new ideas.

Level 4—Synthesis Comprehension
Visualizes
Solves problems
Generates new ideas
Elaborating upon or changing

Level 3—Critical Comprehension
Separates facts from opinion
Judges values of ideas
Develops standards

Level 2—Interpretive Comprehension
Predicts outcomes
Draws conclusions
Understands cause/effect
Able to compare/contrast

Level 1—Literal Comprehension
Can answer basic questions—who (characters), where/when (setting), did what (action), problem (conflict)
Understands vocabulary—context clues, figures of speech, words with multiple meanings
Main ideas
Use of punctuation

Novel Units graphics provide organizers that can serve as comprehension boosters as well as interactive bulletin boards for specific novels.

Cause-Effect

Directions: List the sequence of events in the story. Then mark causes with a C and effects with an E. Remember that many effects cause something else so they might be marked with an E and a C with an arrow to the next effect.

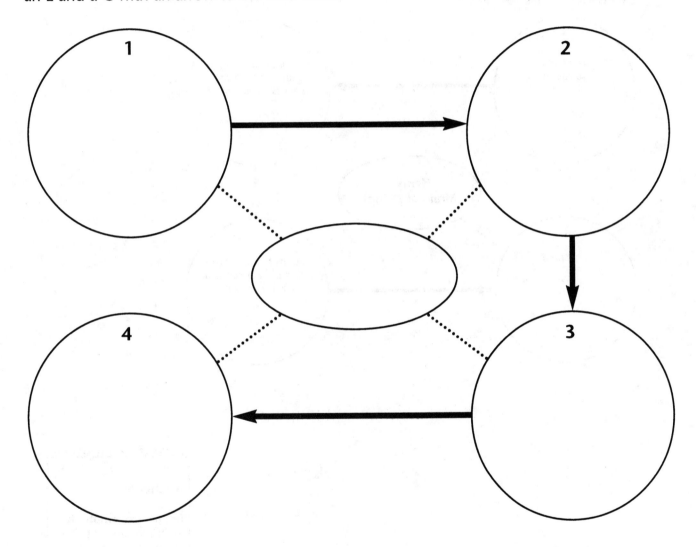

Cause-Effect For *The Red Badge of Courage*
by Stephen Crane

Directions: List the sequence of events. Then mark causes with a C and effects with an E. Remember that many effects cause something else so they might be marked with an E and a C with an arrow to the next effect.

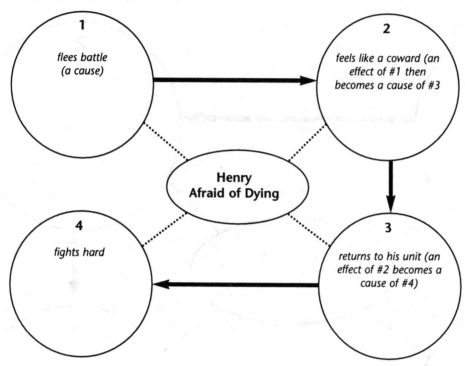

1

flees battle
(a cause)

2

feels like a coward (an effect of #1 then becomes a cause of #3

**Henry
Afraid of Dying**

4

fights hard

3

returns to his unit (an effect of #2 becomes a cause of #4)

Teacher Notes

Teacher can emphasize the importance of sequencing in most cause-effect relation-ships.

Name _____

Cause-Effect

Directions: To plot cause and effect in a story, first list the sequence of events. Then mark causes with a C and effects with an E. Use an arrow from the cause to the effect. Remember that many effects cause something else so they might be marked with an E and a C with an arrow to the next effect.

Events in the story:

1.

2.

3.

4.

5.

6.

7.

8.

9.

10.

Another way to map cause and effect is to look for an effect and then backtrack to the single or multiple causes.

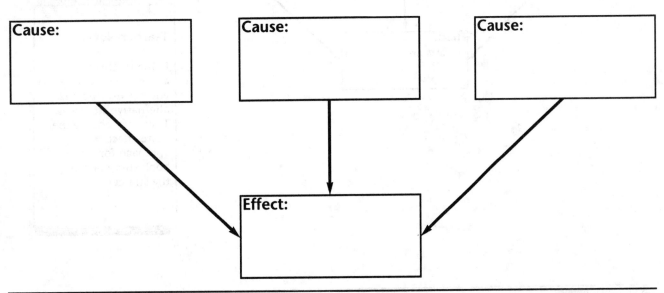

Cause-Effect for *Bridge to Terabithia*

by Katherine Paterson

Directions: To plot cause and effect in a story, first list the sequence of events. Then mark causes with a C and effects with an E. Use an arrow from the cause to the effect. Remember that many effects cause something else so they might be marked with an E and a C with an arrow to the next effect.

Events in the story:

1. *Jesse Aarons practices all summer to be the fastest kid in the fifth grade, only to be beaten by a newcomer, Leslie Burke.*

2. *Leslie and Jess become friends as they build Terabithia, their own secret place.*

3. *Jess gives Leslie Prince Terrien as a Christmas present.*

4. *Leslie is very involved with her father's renovation of their house.*

5. *Leslie goes to the Easter services with Jess's family.*

6. *There's a lot of rain and getting to Terabithia becomes more difficult. Jess is scared swinging across the water. (C)*

7. *Jess goes to the Smithsonian with Miss Edmunds. (C)*

8. *Leslie drowns. (E/C)*

9. *Jess learns about grief; his father helps. (E)*

10. *Jess conquers his fear of water to save his sister. The Burkes move out of the Perkins place. (E)*

Another way to map cause and effect is to look for an effect and then backtrack to the single or multiple causes.

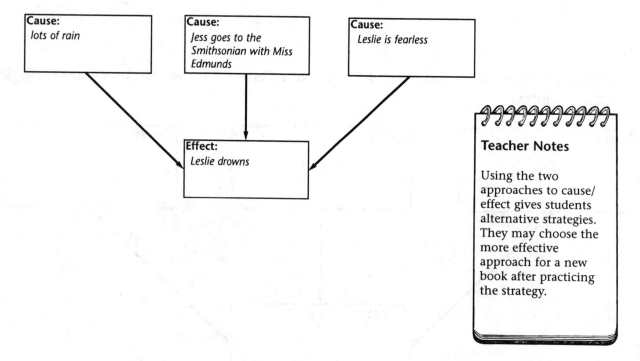

Cause:
lots of rain

Cause:
Jess goes to the Smithsonian with Miss Edmunds

Cause:
Leslie is fearless

Effect:
Leslie drowns

Teacher Notes

Using the two approaches to cause/effect gives students alternative strategies. They may choose the more effective approach for a new book after practicing the strategy.

Name _____

Herringbone

Directions: Using the novel and your imagination, record the answers to the questions on the herringbone form below. (Who was involved? What did these persons do? When did it happen? Where did it happen? How did it happen? Why did it happen?) Add spaces if there are more than two answers to a question. Then write a newspaper article about the incident.

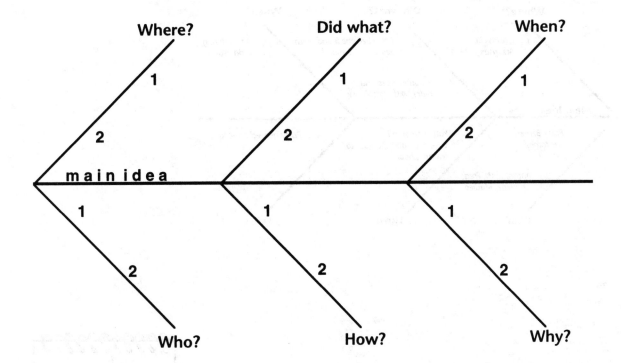

Herringbone for *Summer of My German Soldier*

by Bette Greene

Directions: Using the novel and your imagination, record the answers to the questions on the herringbone form below. (Who was involved? What did these persons do? When did it happen? Where did it happen? How did it happen? Why did it happen?) Add spaces if there are more than two answers to a question. Then write a newspaper article about the incident.

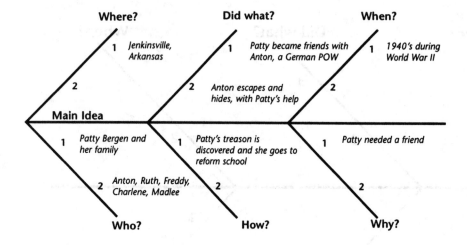

Where?
1 Jenkinsville, Arkansas
2

Did what?
1 Patty became friends with Anton, a German POW
2 Anton escapes and hides, with Patty's help

When?
1 1940's during World War II
2

Main Idea

Who?
1 Patty Bergen and her family
2 Anton, Ruth, Freddy, Charlene, Madlee

How?
1 Patty's treason is discovered and she goes to reform school
2

Why?
1 Patty needed a friend
2

Teacher Notes

Students can investigate newspaper articles to understand the genre prior to writing their article. The herringbone can be completed as a class prior to writing the articles individually.

Fishbone Map

Directions: List the effect (or result) in the dotted box. Consider what are the causes? List cause 1, 2, 3, 4 (as appropriate). Add details to support the causes you list.

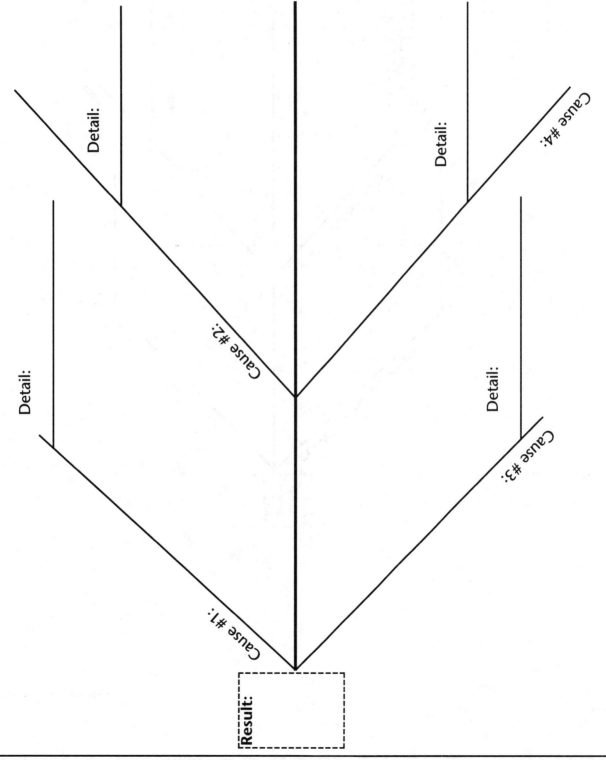

Fishbone Map for *Dicey's Song* by Cynthia Voigt

Directions: List the effect (or result) in the dotted box. Consider what are the causes? List
cause 1, 2, 3, 4 (as appropriate). Add details to support the causes you list.

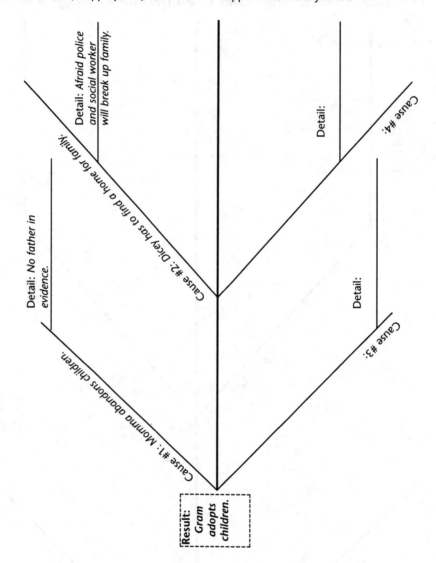

Name _____

Cause/Effect Chart

Directions: When examining the reason for events in a story, we often find that

a) one cause has several results, or

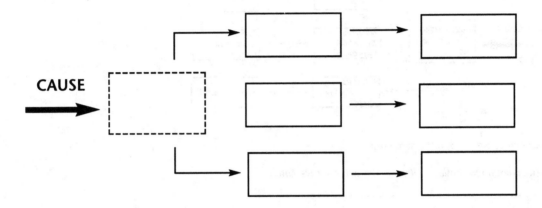

b) several causes lead to the same result.

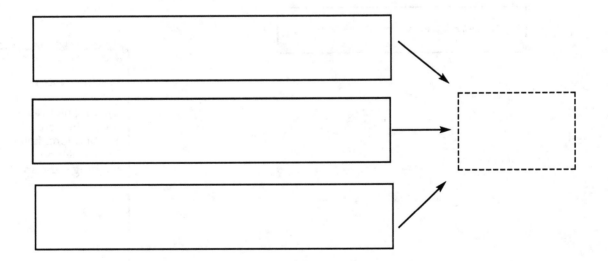

Cause/Effect Chart for

Summer of My German Soldier by Bette Greene

Directions: When examining the reason for events in a story, we often find that

a) one cause has several results, or

The question to consider: How does Patty's friendship for Anton affect the Bergens?

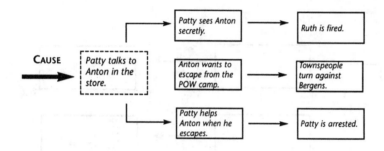

CAUSE → Patty talks to Anton in the store.

- Patty sees Anton secretly. → Ruth is fired.
- Anton wants to escape from the POW camp. → Townspeople turn against Bergens.
- Patty helps Anton when he escapes. → Patty is arrested.

b) several causes lead to the same result.

The question to consider: Why does Patty try to save Anton?

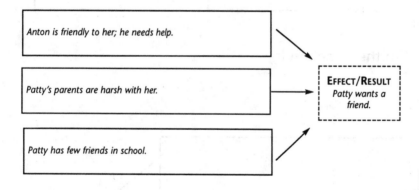

- Anton is friendly to her; he needs help.
- Patty's parents are harsh with her.
- Patty has few friends in school.

→ **EFFECT/RESULT** Patty wants a friend.

Teacher Notes

Phrasing plot cause-effect situations in question form helps focus attention in graphing cause and effect.

Cause/Effect Chart

Directions: Make a flow chart that shows decisions that characters made, the decisions that characters could have made, and the results from each. Use your imagination to speculate on the results of decisions that the character could have made.

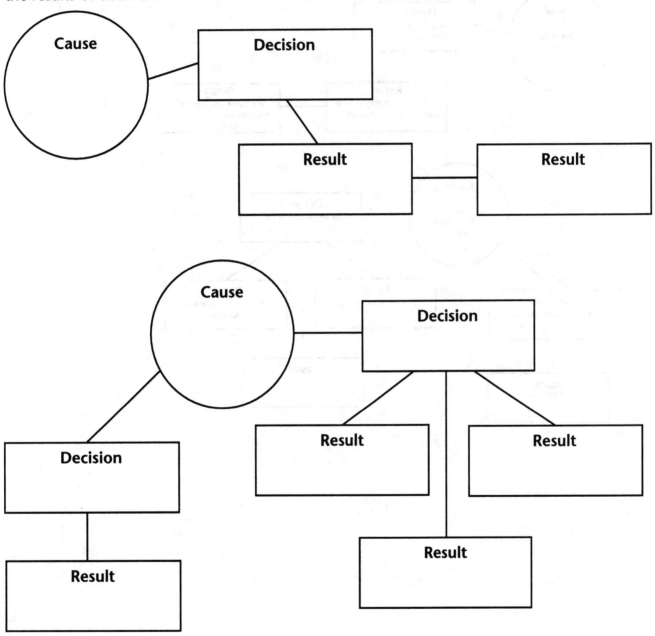

Cause/Effect Chart for *Transport 7-41-R* by T. Degens

Directions: Make a flow chart that shows decisions that characters made, the decisions that characters could have made, and the results from each. Use your imagination to speculate on the results of decisions that the character could have made.

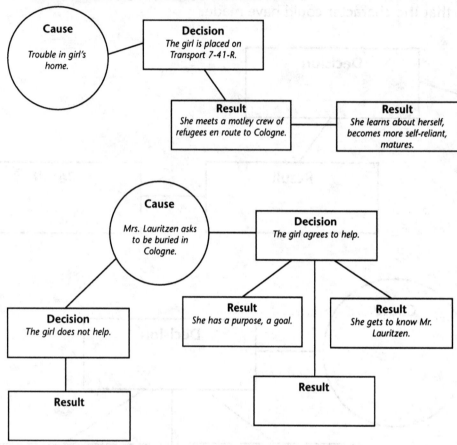

Cause

Trouble in girl's home.

Decision
The girl is placed on Transport 7-41-R.

Result
She meets a motley crew of refugees en route to Cologne.

Result
She learns about herself, becomes more self-reliant, matures.

Cause

Mrs. Lauritzen asks to be buried in Cologne.

Decision
The girl agrees to help.

Decision
The girl does not help.

Result
She has a purpose, a goal.

Result
She gets to know Mr. Lauritzen.

Result

Result

Name _____

Cause and Effect

Directions: Try to trace back to the causes of one of the novel's feelings/moods/attitudes. Then fill in this cause-effect chart.

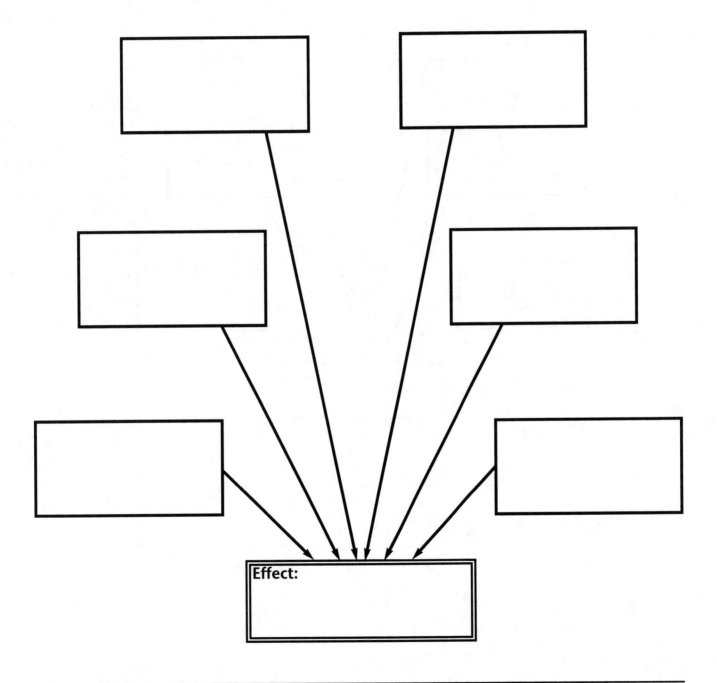

Effect:

Cause and Effect for *Let the Circle Be Unbroken*
by Mildred Taylor

Directions: Try to trace back to the causes of one of the novel's feelings/moods/attitudes. Then fill in this cause-effect chart.

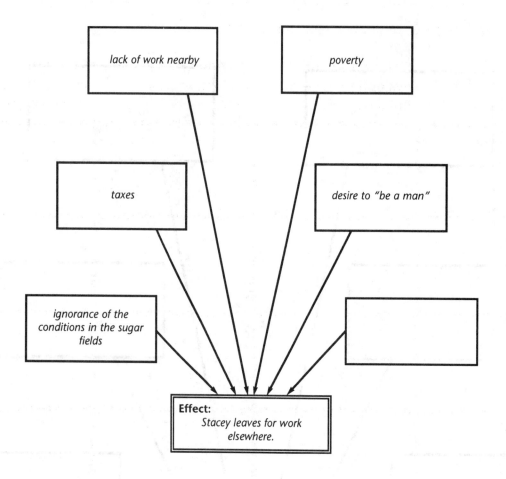

Evaluating your Solutions to a Problem

Directions: State the problem in a short sentence or two.

_____

_____

In the boxes, answer the evaluation questions for each solution idea.

Problem	Criterion #1 for evaluation: Does it break any laws?	Criterion #2 for evaluation: Is it quick enough?	Criterion #3 for evaluation: Does it make you feel good?
Solution #1			
Solution #2			
Solution #3			
Solution #4			
Solution #5			

Evaluating Your Solutions to a Problem for *Brady*
By Jean Fritz

State the problem in a short sentence or two.

Brady's father is injured and it is time for Moss to move to the next stop on the Underground Railroad.

In the boxes, answer the evaluation questions for each solution idea.

Problem	Criterion #1 for evaluation: Does it break any laws?	Criterion #2 for evaluation: Is it quick enough?	Criterion #3 for evaluation: Does it make you feel good?
Solution #1 *Take the horse and buggy and move Moss himself.*	*Yes. Transporting runaway slaves was illegal.*	*Yes*	*Yes*
Solution #2 *Awaken his father for advice.*	*No, but would have to reveal that he knew the truth about the Sermon Hut.*	*Maybe not*	*Maybe not; may feel like a child.*
Solution #3 *Do nothing.*	*No*	*No*	*Maybe not*
Solution #4			
Solution #5			

Teacher Notes

Criterion #1, #2, and #3 may be changed depending on the book and solution. An extra column to include other plusses or minuses or details of each possible solution could be added.

Name _____

DECISION-MAKING

Problem: State the character's problem in the book.

Solutions: Choose 3-7 possible solutions.
    (a)   State each choice in a short sentence.
    (b)   Design 3-5 "criteria" (questions you can ask to measure how good a particular choice may be)
    (c)   Rate the criteria for each solution: **1=yes**   **2=maybe**   **3=no**

CHOICES ↓	CRITERIA				
1.					
2.					
3.					
4.					
5.					
6.					
7.					

Suggested Answers

DECISION-MAKING FOR *BRIDGE TO TERABITHIA*

BY KATHERINE PATERSON

Problem: Janice has stolen May Belle's Twinkies and Jesse has to decide what to do about it.

Solutions: Choose 3-7 possible solutions.
- (a)   State each choice in a short sentence.
- (b)   Design 3-5 "criteria" (questions you can ask to measure how good a particular choice may be)
- (c)   Rate the criteria for each solution: **1=yes   2=maybe   3=no**

CHOICES ↓	CRITERIA				
	Will May Belle be satisfied?	Will I get revenge?	Is this kind?	Will this change Janice?	Will this get me in trouble?
1. Do nothing.					
2. Write a fake love note.					
3. Steal something of Janice's.					
4. Try talking to Janice.					
5.					
6.					
7.					

Teacher Notes

As a follow-up discuss how hard it was to rate the choices and to write effective criteria ques-tions. Once students have completed their evaluation, revise the criteria questions and the possible solutions.

Name _____

Problem-Solving Alternatives

Directions: Choose the particular problems a group of characters or character encounter(s) in a book. Note those problems as well as the book character's solutions on the chart. Then add alternative solutions of your own.

Problem	The Book Character's Solution	Alternative Idea of Yours

Problem-Solving Alternatives for *Shiloh* by Phyllis Reynolds Naylor

Directions: Choose the particular problems a group of characters or character encounter(s) in a book. Note those problems as well as the book character's solutions on the chart. Then add alternative solutions of your own.

Problem	Marty's Solution	Alternative Idea of Yours
Food	saving some of his own meals; getting "leftovers" from shopkeepers	
Storing Food	Hi-C can with plastic lid set in a cool stream	
Secrecy	pen away from the house; scare off Dara Lynn with snake stories and avoid David Howard	
Remembering Lies	concentration	
Guilt About Lies	thinking about Shiloh and the abuse of the dog; later talking to father about it	
Mother's Intuition	ask her to wait to tell Dad	

Name _____

Inference—Flow Chart of Events and Emotions Inferred

Directions: Fill in the boxes in the flow chart with the events portrayed in the story. In the ovals beneath, state what emotion and feeling is inferred.

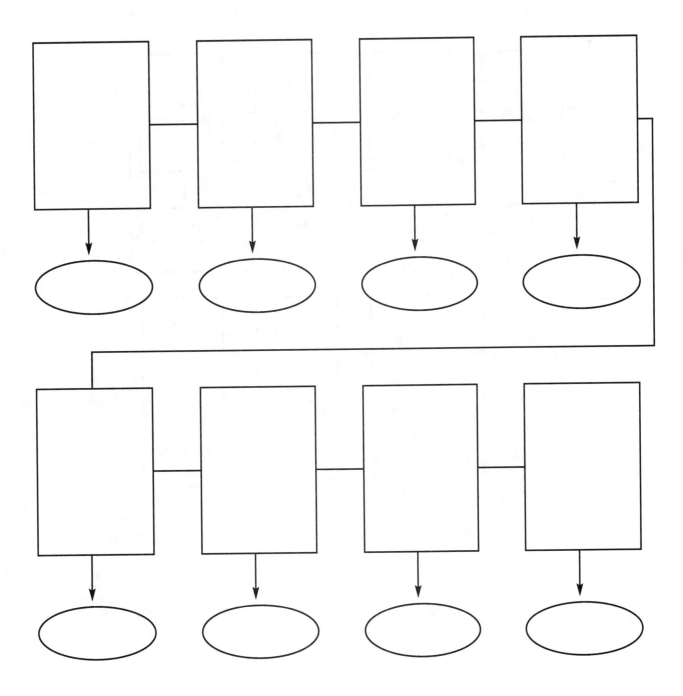

Suggested Answers

Inference—Flow Chart of Events and Emotions Inferred for
Shiloh by Phyllis Reynolds Naylor

Directions: Fill in the boxes in the flow chart with the events portrayed in the story. In the ovals beneath, state what emotion and feeling is inferred.

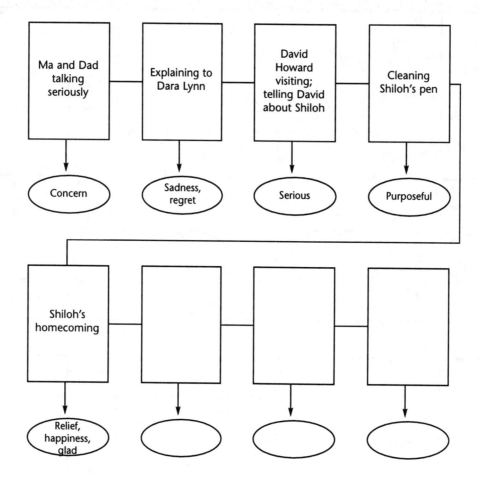

Name _____

Survival Chart

Directions: How does a character survive in the wild? What need does one have to have met in order to survive? Complete the chart below.

Needs	How Character Gets Them
Food	
Water	
Warmth	
Shelter	
Love	
Companionship	
Mental Stimulation	

Survival Chart for *Island of the Blue Dolphins*
by Scott O'Dell

Directions: How does a character survive in the wild? What need does one have to have met in order to survive? Complete the chart below.

Needs	How Character Gets Them
Food	*gull eggs* *seeds* *spearing fish*
Water	*Island of the Blue Dolphins has fresh water—spring, etc. Without fresh water, Karana would need to collect rain water.*
Warmth	*cave*
Shelter	*fence for protection from animals* *rock at one side to protect against wind*
Love	*initially by caring for her brother; later by befriending leader of the wild dogs and naming him Rontu*
Companionship	*looking for a boat to come;* *meets Tutok, an Aleut girl*
Mental Stimulation	*solving her survival problems;* *communicating with Tutok*

Name _____

Solutions

Directions: Stories naturally evolve as a problem happens. The characters then seek a solution for the problem or conflict. This graphic details the solution.

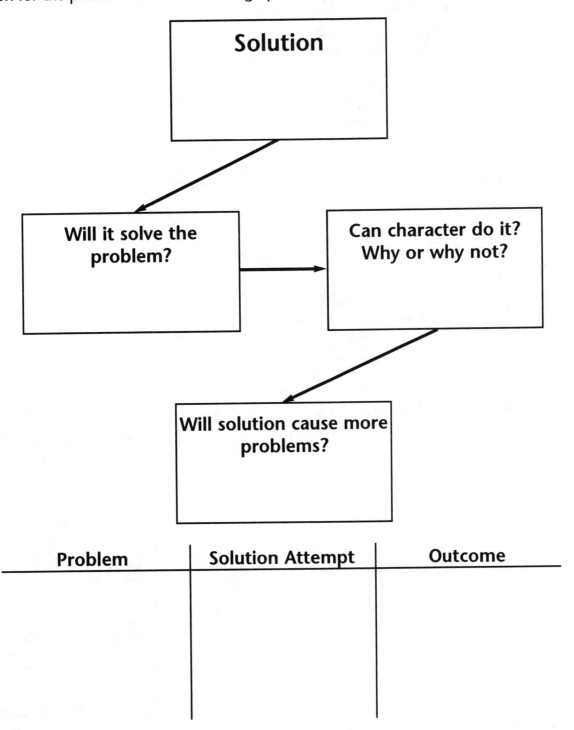

Problem	Solution Attempt	Outcome

Solutions for *Summer of the Monkeys*

by Wilson Rawls

Directions: Stories naturally evolve as a problem happens. The characters then seek a solution for the problem or conflict. This graphic details the solution.

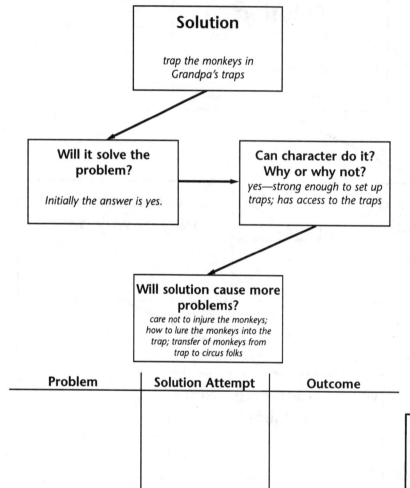

Problem	Solution Attempt	Outcome

Teacher Notes

The graphic focuses particularly on the problem and solution in a story—the crux of the plot, the main reason to have a story.

Many stories have several dead ends with possible solutions before the final resolution. So this graphic might be completed multiple times.

Name _____

Using Dialogue

Directions: Choose a bit of dialogue from the book to investigate. Fill in the chart to describe this way of writing and telling a story.

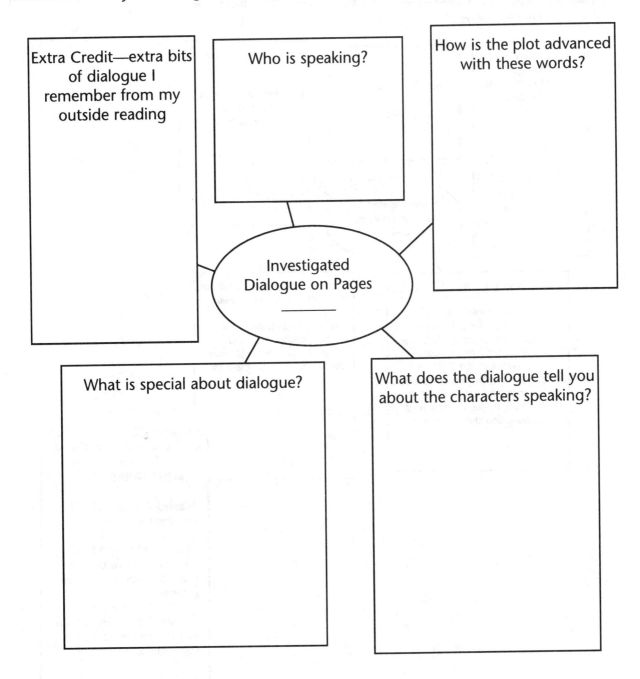

Extra Credit—extra bits of dialogue I remember from my outside reading

Who is speaking?

How is the plot advanced with these words?

Investigated Dialogue on Pages _____

What is special about dialogue?

What does the dialogue tell you about the characters speaking?

Using Dialogue for *Summer of the Monkeys*
by Wilson Rawls

Directions: Choose a bit of dialogue from the book to investigate. Fill in the chart to describe this way of writing and telling a story.

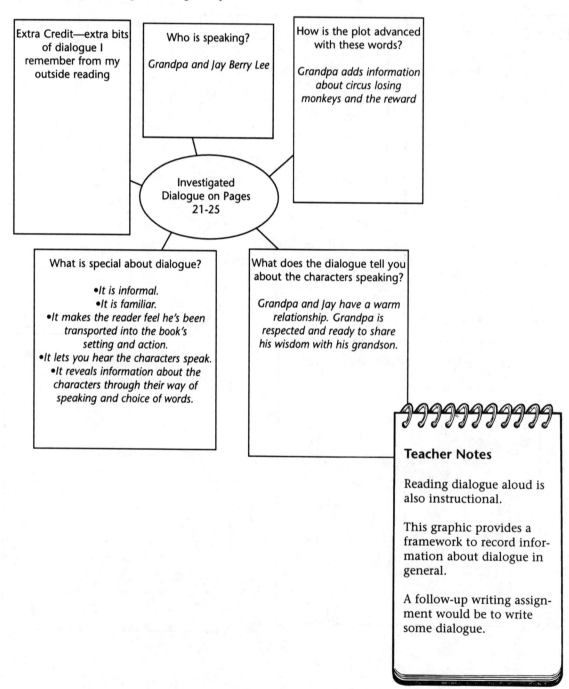

Extra Credit—extra bits of dialogue I remember from my outside reading

Who is speaking?

Grandpa and Jay Berry Lee

How is the plot advanced with these words?

Grandpa adds information about circus losing monkeys and the reward

Investigated Dialogue on Pages 21-25

What is special about dialogue?

•*It is informal.*
•*It is familiar.*
•*It makes the reader feel he's been transported into the book's setting and action.*
•*It lets you hear the characters speak.*
•*It reveals information about the characters through their way of speaking and choice of words.*

What does the dialogue tell you about the characters speaking?

Grandpa and Jay have a warm relationship. Grandpa is respected and ready to share his wisdom with his grandson.

Teacher Notes

Reading dialogue aloud is also instructional.

This graphic provides a framework to record information about dialogue in general.

A follow-up writing assignment would be to write some dialogue.

Assessment with Graphic Organizers

Overview: Graphic organizers are used many ways in the classroom across the curriculum. Assessment varies with the particular purpose at the time. For example, expected results and therefore assessment will vary between a prewriting use and a summative application.

It is important to remember that the information and ideas generated and recorded are much more important than the particular graphic organizer itself.

Different rubrics are provided herein for various uses of graphic organizers.

In some instances, there are places provided for student and teacher ratings. Asking students to rate themselves first encourages self-evaluation and monitoring as well as reflective learning.

Name _____

Use: Brainstorming, Opening the Mind
for Creative Thought, Thinking Visually

Focus: Ideas presented are on the topic.	30	25	15
Organization: Ideas are grouped as needed. Groupings are clear and appropriate. Ideas are connected as needed.	30	25	15
Details: Desired number of responses are included.	30	23	15
Mechanics: Spelling and usage are correct.	10	7	5
Additional Points	—	—	—
TOTAL	100	80	50

Comments:

(Evidence of divergent thinking and new creative notions should be rewarded in the additional points section.)

Name _____

Use: Prereading Evaluation Form

	Student Rating	**Teacher Rating**
Focus: Student writes a clear overview if required.	_____	_____
Organization: Ideas are grouped appropriately.	_____	_____
Detail: Multiple ideas are provided.	_____	_____
Mechanics: Spelling, capitalization, and usage are correct.	_____	_____
Sentence/Phrase Structure: Student avoids run-ons and phraseology is comprehensible.	_____	_____
Total Effect	_____	_____
Aptness of Thought: Ideas are on topic.	_____	_____

Comments:

Name _____

Use: Prewriting Evaluation Form

	Student Rating	**Teacher Rating**
Focus: Ideas are on point and can be developed into a finished written piece.	_____	_____
Evaluation: Inappropriate or unusable ideas have been deleted.	_____	_____
Organization: Ideas are grouped and sequenced appropriately.	_____	_____
Detail: Multiple ideas are recorded displaying effort and depth of thought as well as time on task.	_____	_____
Writer's Craft: Ideas are appropriate for the particular writing vehicle—narrative, expository, persuasive.	_____	_____

Comments:

Name _____

Use: To Record Data

	Student Rating	Teacher Rating
Focus: Ideas are apt and recorded in the appropriate place.	_____	_____
Detail: Desired *number* of responses are included.	_____	_____
Mechanics: Spelling, capitalization, and usage are correct.	_____	_____
Evaluation and Synthesis: Important and crucial ideas are included.	_____	_____

Comments:

Use: With a Cooperative Group

Students will complete this form to record their work together with a graphic organizer.

Name:_____

Assignment: _____

Date: _____

For this assignment, our group including _____, _____,

and _____ used a graphic organizer.

Please particularly note these things about our work: _____

_____

_____.

We had these problems: _____

_____

_____.

We need help on: _____

_____

_____.

Signed,

Name _____

Use: To Organize Ideas for Study and
Research, Remembering

Focus: Important and critical ideas are included.	30	25	15
Organization: Grouping is appropriate—hierarchical or otherwise.	30	25	15
Details: Accuracy, sufficient number.	30	23	15
Mechanics: Spelling and usage are correct.	10	7	5
TOTAL	100	80	50

Comments:

LITERATURE GUIDES

Novel Units™ Teacher Guides and Student Packets

Why have Novel Units been the teachers' first choice for over 10 years? Because teachers recognize and appreciate that the Teacher Guides and Student Packets

- include everything expected from a "literature guide," plus a whole lot more.
- are easy-to-use and include everything you need to teach a novel.
- focus on proven time-savers.
- contain innovative and engaging lesson plans and student activities that foster higher-level thinking skills, using the latest in reading strategies and graphic organizers.
- present new ways to teach reading, writing, thinking, and the love for literature.
- are created by teachers for teachers.
- focus directly on the novel content, unlike many of the guides available.
- maintain consistent lesson format, which is a great time-saver when preparing to teach a new novel.
- most content-based pages of all the guides available.
- offer the largest selection of literature guides—over 525 classic, contemporary, award-winning, and Spanish titles.
- provide a complete, comprehensive teaching unit, even though they have been specifically designed to be successfully used alone.

Novel Units™ provide new ways to teach reading, writing, thinking, and the love for literature.

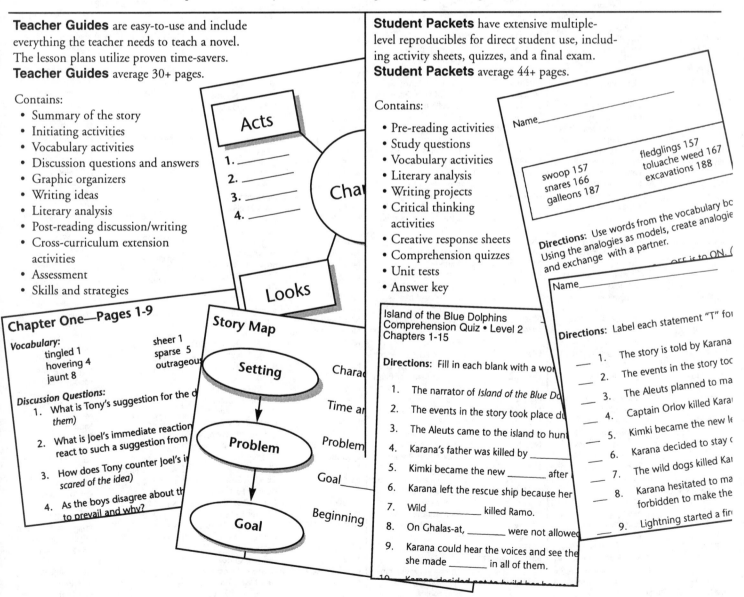

Teacher Guides are easy-to-use and include everything the teacher needs to teach a novel. The lesson plans utilize proven time-savers.
Teacher Guides average 30+ pages.

Contains:
- Summary of the story
- Initiating activities
- Vocabulary activities
- Discussion questions and answers
- Graphic organizers
- Writing ideas
- Literary analysis
- Post-reading discussion/writing
- Cross-curriculum extension activities
- Assessment
- Skills and strategies

Student Packets have extensive multiple-level reproducibles for direct student use, including activity sheets, quizzes, and a final exam.
Student Packets average 44+ pages.

Contains:
- Pre-reading activities
- Study questions
- Vocabulary activities
- Literary analysis
- Writing projects
- Critical thinking activities
- Creative response sheets
- Comprehension quizzes
- Unit tests
- Answer key

Novel Units™ Available

Grades 1-2

NU4059	Amazing Bone
NU0231	Amelia Bedelia
NU2609	Aminal
NU2781	Anansi the Spider
NU2676	Arthur's Honey Bear
NU0029	Bargain for Frances
NU4075	Beady Bear
NU461X	Benjamin Brody's Backyard Bag
NU4717	Biggest Bear
NU0045	Corduroy; Pocket for Corduroy (2 books)
NU2706	Curious George
NU2625	Dandelion
NU2692	Danny and the Dinosaur
NU2072	Frog & Toad All Year; Frog & Toad Are Friends; Frog & Toad Together (3 books)
NU4725	Funny Little Women
NU0096	Ira Sleeps Over
NU3281	Legend of the Bluebonnet
NU3273	Lyle, Lyle Crocodile
NU4733	Madeline's Rescue
NU2307	Make Way for Ducklings
NU2595	Mike Mulligan and His Steam Shovel
NU0320	Miss Nelson is Missing, Miss Nelson is Back (2 books)
NU2587	Miss Rumphius
NU4016	Mr. Rabbit and the Lovely Present
NU329X	Mud Pony
NU2633	Nate the Great and the Sticky Case
NU4741	Once a Mouse
NU2498	One Fine Day
NU4156	One in the Middle is the Green Kangaroo
NU4571	Ox-Cart Man
NU475X	Paper Bag Princess
NU2641	Perfect the Pig
NU2617	Pinkerton, Behave!
NU1963	Polar Express
NU2668	Runaway Bunny
NU4768	Snowy Day
NU2013	Stone Soup
NU265X	Story of Ferdinand
NU3303	Story of Jumping Mouse
NU279X	Strega Nona
NU2684	Swimmy; Frederick (2 books)
NU0193	Sylvester and the Magic Pebble
NU4113	Tales of Oliver Pig
NU4296	Tenth Good Thing About Barney
NU3656	There's a Nightmare in My Closet
NU0215	Tikki Tikki Tembo
NU2803	Ugly Duckling
NU4776	Uncle Willie and the Soup Kitchen
NU0223	Where the Wild Things Are
NU4784	Why Mosquitoes Buzz in People's Ears
NU4563	Widow's Broom

Grades 3-4

NU6485	Almost Starring Skinnybones
NU2722	Anastasia Krupnik
NU6450	BFG
NU6949	Basil of Baker Street
NU2811	Be a Perfect Person in Just Three Days
NU1882	Bear Called Paddington
NU7848 NU7856SP	Beauty
NU4164	Beezus and Ramona

NU3958	Ben and Me
NU1971 NU7015SP	Best Christmas Pageant Ever
NU7228	Blossom Promise
NU4024	Can't You Make Them Behave, King George?
NU1904 NU7023SP	Charlie and the Chocolate Factory
NU0266 NU6302SP	Charlotte's Web
NU6523	Chocolate by Hershey: A Story About Milton S. Hershey
NU1769 NU7031SP	Chocolate Fever
NU0479 NU8259SP	Chocolate Touch
NU6477	Class Clown
NU6752	Country Artist: A Story About Beatrix Potter
NU2390	Courage of Sarah Noble
NU3966 NU8356SP	Cricket in Times Square
NU0487	Cybil War
NU3877	Ellen Tebbits
NU282X	Encyclopedia Brown
NU2560	Enormous Egg
NU2501	Fairy Rebel
NU3680	Family Under the Bridge
NU0495	Fantastic Mr. Fox
NU6124	Flunking of Joshua T. Bates
NU4431	Fourth Grade Celebrity
NU4423	Freaky Friday
NU0088 NU8224SP	Freckle Juice
NU6008 NU6016SP	Friendship
NU668X	Grain of Rice
NU7236	Grand Escape
NU4253	Henry and the Clubhouse
NU6019	Henry Huggins
NU3869	Hundred Penny Box
NU332X	I Sailed with Columbus
NU4512	Isabelle the Itch
NU4539	J. T.
NU055X NU4873SP	James and the Giant Peach
NU3311	Jumanji
NU6353	Kid in the Red Jacket
NU2439 NU704XSP	Lion, the Witch, and the Wardrobe
NU0304 NU7058SP	Little House in the Big Woods
NU0312 NU8348SP	Little House on the Prairie
NU2846	Littles
NU0576	Long Winter
NU5896	Matilda
NU6469	Maurice's Room
NU6024 NU6032SP	M. C. Higgins
NU2749 NU7066SP	Mouse and the Motorcycle
NU6973	Mystery at Loon Lake
NU6027	Not-Just-Anybody Family
NU6531	Oh, the Places He Went: A Story About Dr. Seuss
NU6132	On the Banks of Plum Creek
NU6981	123 Zoo Mystery
NU1998 NU7074SP	Owls in the Family
NU3338	Pecos Bill
NU0363	Pippi Longstocking
NU6744	Raggin! A Story About Scott Joplin
NU1734	Ralph S. Mouse
NU3699	Ramona and Her Father
NU4482 NU7082SP	Ramona Quimby, Age 8
NU444X	Ramona the Brave
NU4393	Ramona the Pest
NU6035	Ribsy
NU1742	Runaway Ralph
NU1785 NU6310SP	Sadako and the Thousand Paper Cranes
NU0401	Sam, Bangs, and Moonshine
NU2471 NU6329SP	Sarah, Plain and Tall

NU2757	Secret Life of the Underwear Champ
NU4997	Silver
NU6040 NU6059SP	Skinny Bones
NU6558	Skylark
NU2854	Snow Treasure
NU5861	Sophie and the Sidewalk Man
NU699X	Spider Kane and the Mystery Under the May-Apple
NU7880	Stinker From Space
NU0630 NU6337SP	Stone Fox
NU671X	Stories Julian Tells
NU4520	Stuart Little
NU1750	Superfudge
NU2714 NU7090SP	Tales of a Fourth Grade Nothing
NU3346 NU8267SP	Taste of Blackberries
NU4105	There's a Boy in the Girls' Bathroom
NU6140	Trouble with Tuck
NU0673 NU7104SP	Trumpet of the Swan
NU1793	Velveteen Rabbit
NU7244	WANTED. . . Mud Blossom
NU3885	What's the Big Idea, Ben Franklin?
NU3796	Where Was Patrick Henry on the 29th of May?
NU0894 NU7112SP	Whipping Boy
NU3818	Who's that Stepping on Plymouth Rock?
NU7864 NU7872SP	Wings
NU3702	Wish Giver

Grades 5-6

NU3451	Abel's Island
NU6590	Alan and Naomi
NU0436	Babe the Gallant Pig
NU5621 NU563XSP	Ballad of Lucy Whipple
NU5559 NU5567SP	Barn
NU7252	Bearstone
NU5575 NU5583SP	Belle Prater's Boy
NU7899	Big Wander
NU8399 NU8771SP	Bigger
NU2862	Black Pearl
NU0940	Black Stallion
NU6957	Bodies in the Bessledorf Hotel
NU7902	Boggart
NU069X	Borrowers
NU248X NU4881SP	Bridge to Terabithia
NU0452	Brighty of the Grand Canyon
NU7910	Bristle Face
NU7260	Bronze Bow
NU8984 NU8992SP	Bull Run
NU2005 NU7120SP	Bunnicula
NU587X	Burning Questions of Bingo Brown
NU8100 NU8119SP	By the Great Horn Spoon
NU2315	Cabin Faced West
NU2552	Caddie Woodlawn
NU7279	Canyon Winter
NU3710 NU8305SP	Castle in the Attic
NU2870	Cat Ate My Gymsuit
NU7929 NU7937SP	Catherine, Called Birdy
NU5888	Charley Skedaddle
NU7945	Charlie Pippin
NU6418	Click! A Story About George Eastman
NU0967	Come Sing, Jimmy Jo
NU6701	Cracker Jackson
NU5729 NU5737SP	Crazy Horse Electric Game
NU7953 NU7961SP	Crazy Lady!
NU7287	Daphne's Book
NU2579 NU7139SP	Dear Mr. Henshaw
NU797X	Dear Napoleon, I Know You're Dead, but …
NU6965	Dew Drop Dead

NU2889 NU5241SP	Door in the Wall
NU5004 NU8240SP	Egypt Game
NU6261 NU627XSP	Ella Enchanted
NU6515	Eternal Spring of Mr. Ito
NU7295	Face on the Milk Carton
NU6612	Facts and Fictions of Minna Pratt
NU1890	Fighting Ground
NU6655	Fledgling
NU8208 NU881XSP	Flip Flop Girl
NU2838	Forgotten Door
NU6582	Friedrich
NU2269 NU7147SP	From the Mixed-Up Files of Mrs. Basil E. Frankweiler
NU0762	Gentle Ben
NU6159	Golden Goblet
NU458X	Great Brain
NU6736	Gruel and Unusual Punishment
NU3494	Harriet the Spy
NU6067 NU6075SP	Harry Potter and the Sorcerer's Stone
NU2897	Homer Price
NU0789	Horse in the Attic
NU2048 NU7155SP	How to Eat Fried Worms
NU1807	Hundred Dresses
NU1815	I, Houdini Auto-biography of a Hamster
NU3443 NU833XSP	In the Year of the Boar and Jackie Robinson
NU2250 NU6930SP	Indian in the Cupboard
NU2528 NU489XSP	Island of the Blue Dolphins
NU1017	It's Like This, Cat
NU6647	Jar of Dreams
NU2382	Jelly Belly
NU4709	Jennifer, Hecate, Macbeth, William McKinley, and Me, Elizabeth
NU8402 NU878XSP	Jeremy Thatcher, Dragon Hatcher
NU7988	Jericho's Journey
NU7309	Jim Ugly
NU6434	Leaves in October
NU6604	Let the Circle Be Unbroken
NU8429 NU8801SP	Letters from Rifka
NU644X NU6458SP	Lily's Crossing
NU6288 NU6296SP	Long Way From Chicago
NU5012	Lottery Rose
NU5020	Lyddie
NU3486 NU6043SP	Maniac Magee
NU6426	Mark T-W-A-I-N! A Story About Samuel Clemens
NU6671	Midnight Fox
NU6620	Midnight Horse
NU7007	Missing Gator of Gumbo Limbo
NU590X	Missing May
NU7317	Monkey Island
NU7325	Moonshiner's Son
NU6361	Mr. Blue Jeans: A Story About Levi Strauss
NU1777 NU7163SP	Mr. Popper's Penguins
NU2765	Mr. Revere and I
NU7333	My Daniel
NU6566	Mystery of the Cupboard
NU654X	Night of the Twisters
NU2544 NU6051SP	Number the Stars
NU0819	Old Yeller
NU3354	On My Honor
NU1076	One-Eyed Cat
NU1939	Otis Spofford
NU2900	Phantom Tollbooth
NU0592	Phillip Hall likes me. I reckon maybe.
NU0824 NU8275SP	Pinballs
NU637X	Pocketful of Goobers: A Story About George Washington Carver
NU5680 NU5699SP	Poppy

SP indicates Student Packet for this title.

Novel Units™ Available

Code	SP Code	Title
NU8410	NU8798SP	Question of Trust
NU0606		Rabbit Hill
NU5918		Rachel Carson: Pioneer of Ecology
NU5761	NU577XSP	Racing the Sun
NU0835		Rascal
NU7341		Red Cap
NU8003		Rescue Josh McGuire
NU2323		Return of the Indian
NU0851	NU525XSP	Roll of Thunder, Hear My Cry
NU6167		Sandra Day O'Connor: Justice For All
NU735X		Search For Delicious
NU0622	NU5268SP	Secret Garden
NU203X		Secret of the Indian
NU5926		Shades of Gray
NU4245	NU606XSP	Shiloh
NU2919		Sing Down the Moon
NU9026	NU9034SP	Sparrow Hawk Red
NU6083	NU6091SP	Stranded
NU5934		Strider
NU0657		Summer of the Monkeys
NU1149	NU8313SP	Summer of the Swans
NU6698		There's a Bat in Bunk Five
NU7368		There's a Girl in My Hammerlock
NU6728		Thunder Rolling in the Mountains
NU4350		Trouble River
NU4792	NU8291SP	True Confessions of Charlotte Doyle
NU251X	NU4903SP	Tuck Everlasting
NU9042	NU9050SP	Under the Blood Red Sun
NU6574		Upstairs Room
NU9352	NU9360SP	View From Saturday
NU5039		Voyage of the Frog
NU5942		War Comes to Willy Freeman
NU1912		War With Grandpa
NU6105	NU6113SP	Watsons Go To Birmingham
NU4806		Weasel
NU5950		When Hitler Stole Pink Rabbit
NU7376		Which Way Freedom?
NU3400		White Mountains
NU2927		Who Really Killed Cock Robin?
NU2080		Wind in the Willows
NU5969		Winter Room

Grades 7-8

Code	SP Code	Title
NU4342		Acorn People
NU0916	NU4911SP	Across Five Aprils
NU3567	NU5284SP	Adventures of Tom Sawyer
NU0983	NU6078SP	Anne Frank: Diary of a Young Girl
NU3419		Anne of Green Gables
NU119X		April Morning
NU4814		Banner in the Sky
NU0924		Beat the Turtle Drum
NU0932		Big Red
NU1203		Big Wave
NU1483		Bless the Beasts and the Children
NU5826	NU5834SP	Bomb
NU6639		Brady
NU2455	NU492XSP	Call It Courage
NU1386	NU5292SP	Call of the Wild
NU4822		Canyons
NU3141	NU4121SP	Cay
NU1394		Cheaper by the Dozen
NU7384		Children of the River
NU6175		Christmas Carol
NU1211	NU6086SP	Contender
NU3931	NU394XSP	Day No Pigs Would Die
NU1408		Deathwatch
NU4385		Dicey's Song
NU3427		Dogsong

Code	SP Code	Title
NU0738		Dragonwings
NU0991		Farewell to Manzanar
NU4083	NU4091SP	Flowers for Algernon
NU900X	NU9018SP	Freak the Mighty
NU1513		Gentlehands
NU6183	NU7171SP	Giver
NU4228	NU8372SP	Great Gilly Hopkins
NU1238	NU4938SP	Hatchet
NU7996		Haymeadow
NU6121	NU613XSP	Heaven
NU2536	NU8283SP	Hobbit
NU6148	NU6156SP	Holes
NU1246		Homecoming
NU5160	NU8321SP	House of Dies Drear
NU580X	NU5818SP	I am the Cheese
NU1424		I Heard the Owl Call My Name
NU2293		I Know What You Did Last Summer
NU1254		Incident at Hawk's Hill
NU4687	NU4695SP	Incredible Journey
NU2021		Izzy, Willy-Nilly
NU1262	NU8364SP	Jacob Have I Loved
NU1270	NU5306SP	Johnny Tremain
NU4857		Journey
NU1025	NU8216SP	Julie of the Wolves
NU377X	NU3788SP	Just Dial a Number
NU1947	NU3435SP	Killing Mr. Griffin
NU1033		King of the Wind
NU1432		Language of the Goldfish
NU4660	NU4679SP	Light in the Forest
NU5179		Lincoln: A Photobiography
NU630X	NU6318SP	Little Women
NU6164	NU6172SP	Man Who Was Poe
NU8011	NU802XSP	Midwife's Apprentice
NU1831	NU5314SP	Miracle Worker
NU1041		Moves Make the Man
NU2730	NU5322SP	Mrs. Frisby and the Rats of NIMH
NU380X	NU8232SP	My Brother Sam is Dead
NU1068	NU4946SP	My Side of the Mountain
NU7392		No Promises in the Wind
NU7406		Nothing But the Truth
NU5893	NU5907SP	Out of the Dust
NU3621	NU4067SP	Outsiders
NU3257	NU3265SP	Pearl
NU3893	NU3907SP	Pigman
NU198X		Pistachio Prescription
NU4407	NU4415SP	Red Pony
NU5977		Riddle of Penncroft Farm
NU5985		Rifles for Watie
NU6116		River
NU8186	NU8194SP	Samurai's Tale
NU4865		Sarah Bishop
NU2935		Scorpions
NU6326	NU6334SP	Shabanu: Daughter of the Wind
NU1084		Shadow of a Bull
NU2420	NU4954SP	Sign of the Beaver
NU1335		Slave Dancer
NU184X		Snow Bound
NU5788	NU5796SP	So Far from the Bamboo Grove
NU1459		Solitary Blue
NU1106	NU4962SP	Sounder
NU1114		Soup
NU5702	NU5710SP	Staying Fat for Sarah Byrnes
NU5993		Stonewall
NU7414		Streams to the River, River to the Sea
NU1122		Summer of Fear
NU1130		Summer of My German Soldier
NU1955		Tiger Eyes
NU8844	NU8852SP	Tiger, Tiger, Burning Bright
NU7422		Timothy of the Cay
NU8860	NU8879SP	Toughing It
NU6000		Traitor: The Case of Benedict Arnold
NU6493		Transport 7-41-R

Code	SP Code	Title
NU1343		Treasure Island
NU3761		Twenty-One Balloons
NU7708	NU7716SP	Walk Two Moons
NU8143	NU8151SP	Weirdo
NU7430	NU8038SP	West Against the Wind
NU4644	NU4652SP	Westing Game
NU4229	NU4237SP	When the Legend Die
NU6342	NU6350SP	Where the Lilies Bloom
NU2447	NU4907SP	Where the Red Fern Grows
NU3362	NU5276SP	White Fang
NU2463	NU5349SP	Witch of Blackbird Pond
NU4172		Woodsong
NU1181	NU4989SP	Wrinkle in Time
NU8887	NU8895SP	Z for Zachariah

Grades 9-12

Code	SP Code	Title
NU1823	NU3087SP	Adventures of Huckleberry Finn
NU6191	NU6205SP	All Quiet on the Western Front
NU9131	NU914XSP	All the Pretty Horses
NU6180	NU6199SP	Animal Dreams
NU3052	NU3060SP	Animal Farm
NU7449	NU7457SP	Antigone
NU5532	NU5540SP	As I Lay Dying
NU5047	NU5055SP	As You Like It
NU8909	NU8917SP	Bean Trees
NU9158	NU9166SP	Billy Budd
NU6202	NU6210SP	Black Boy
NU8062	NU8070SP	Bless Me, Ultima
NU4458	NU4466SP	Brave New World
NU5063	NU5071SP	Cannery Row
NU9190	NU9204SP	Canterbury Tales
NU4490	NU4504SP	Catcher in the Rye
NU2064	NU6299SP	Chocolate War
NU7465	NU7473SP	Chosen
NU508X	NU5098SP	Cold Sassy Tree
NU363X	NU3648SP	Crucible
NU3540	NU3559SP	Cry, the Beloved Country
NU6213	NU6221SP	Cyrano de Bergerac
NU7481	NU749XSP	Dandelion Wine
NU5101	NU511XSP	David Copperfield
NU1491		Death Be Not Proud
NU1858	NU3850SP	Death of a Salesman
NU8925	NU8933SP	Doll's House/ Hedda Gabler
NU6229	NU6237SP	Downriver
NU1505		Effect of Gamma Rays on Man-in-the-Moon Marigolds
NU5128	NU5136SP	Ethan Frome
NU301X	NU3028SP	Fahrenheit 451
NU6369	NU6377SP	Fallen Angels
NU4547	NU4555SP	Farewell to Arms
NU7503	NU7511SP	Frankenstein
NU1866	NU3370SP	Glass Menagerie
NU2994	NU3001SP	Grapes of Wrath
NU5144	NU5152SP	Great Expectations
NU3168	NU3176SP	Great Gatsby
NU9212	NU9220SP	Gulliver's Travels
NU4180	NU4199SP	Hamlet
NU3729	NU3737SP	Heart is a Lonely Hunter
NU6245	NU6253SP	Hear of Darkness/ Secret Sharer
NU136X		Hiroshima
NU4830	NU5591SP	House on Mango Street
NU4849	NU6345SP	I Know Why the Caged Bird Sings
NU752X	NU7538SP	Iliad
NU5605	NU5613SP	Ironman
NU7546	NU7554SP	Ishi, Last of His Tribe
NU4628	NU4636SP	Jane Eyre
NU8941	NU895XSP	Joy Luck Club
NU3036	NU3044SP	Julius Caesar
NU9239	NU9247SP	King Lear
NU7562	NU7570SP	Les Miserables
NU5648	NU5656SP	Long Day's Journey Into Night
NU3834	NU3842SP	Lord of the Flies
NU4369	NU4377SP	Macbeth
NU5745	NU5753SP	Madame Bovary
NU3508	NU3516SP	Mayor of Casterbridge

Code	SP Code	Title
NU5664	NU5672SP	Merchant of Venice
NU5187	NU5195SP	Midsummer Night's Dream
NU9255	NU9263SP	Much Ado About Nothing
NU7589	NU7597SP	My Antonia
NU816X	NU8178SP	Mythology
NU623X	NU6248SP	Native Son
NU8046	NU8054SP	Night
NU413X	NU4148SP	1984
NU7600	NU7619SP	Odyssey
NU7627	NU7635SP	Oedipus the King
NU1874	NU3109SP	Of Mice and Men
NU4032	NU4040SP	Old Man and the Sea
NU5209	NU5217SP	Othello
NU6256	NU6264SP	Our Town
NU7643	NU7651SP	Portrait of the Artist as a Young Man
NU766X	NU7678SP	Pride and Prejudice
NU9271	NU928XSP	Pygmalion
NU3125	NU3133SP	Raisin in the Sun
NU346X	NU3478SP	Red Badge of Courage
NU3745	NU3753SP	Romeo and Juliet
NU1440		Rumble Fish
NU3389	NU3397SP	Scarlet Letter
NU6385	NU6393SP	Scarlet Pimpernel
NU8968	NU8976SP	Sense and Sensibility
NU3990	NU4008SP	Separate Peace
NU2773	NU5330SP	Shane
NU6407	NU6415SP	Slam!
NU5842	NU5850SP	Snow Falling on Cedars
NU8828	NU8836SP	Song of Be
NU9379	NU9387SP	Song of Solomon
NU9298	NU9301SP	Stranger
NU4326	NU4334SP	Tale of Two Cities
NU7686	NU7694SP	Taming of the Shrew
NU6272	NU6280SP	Tempest
NU4261	NU427XSP	Tess of the D'Urbervilles
NU1467		Tex
NU5225	NU5233SP	That Was Then, This Is Now
NU8089	NU8097SP	Their Eyes Were Watching God
NU8127	NU8135SP	Things Fall Apart
NU1572	NU3079SP	To Kill a Mockingbird
NU931X	NU9328SP	Turn of the Screw
NU5869	NU5877SP	Twelfth Night
NU6423	NU6431SP	Watership Down
NU4598	NU4601SP	Wuthering Heights
NU9336	NU9344SP	Yellow Raft in Blue Water

Additional Products

Code	Title
NU783XRH	Graphic Organizer Collection
NU5885RH	Holocaust: Study Guide
NU5966RH	Novel News
NU8437RH	Reacting To Literature: Writing Activities for Every Book Gr. 6-8
NU5524RH	Reacting To Literature: Writing Activities for Every Book Gr. 9-12
NU5958RH	Tackling Literary Terms
NU9395RH	Teaching Viewing
NU8453RH	Writing Projects for Literature

Please contact us if you do not see the title you are looking for. New titles are continually being added.

SP indicates Student Packet for this title.

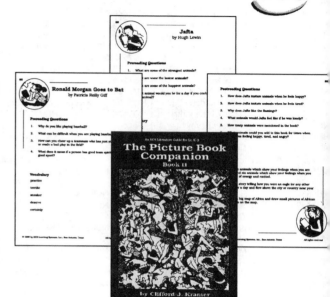

Picture Book Companion
by Clifford J. Kramer

Each book contains 45 classroom-tested lesson guides to accompany the best in children's picture books.

Imagine being able to create a community of readers in your classroom. The Picture Book Companion series is designed to do just that.

- Lessons will motivate students in reading and help them develop reading as a lifelong habit.

- Every children's book discussed in The Picture Book Companion series is easy to find—from old favorites to exciting new titles.

- A must for every K-3 classroom.

"I'm so glad I found you. Your company's products are great." OH

Features

Each lesson includes prereading questions, vocabulary words, postreading questions, and activities for brainstorming, creative writing, and art.

ECS1227	**Easy Order Set of All 3 Books**				**$36.9**
ECS9587	Picture Book Companion 1	96pp.	Gr. K-3	$12.95
ECS9595	Picture Book Companion 2	96pp.	Gr. K-3	$12.95
ECS9641	Picture Book Companion 3	96pp.	Gr. K-3	$12.95

Book I
Abiyoyo
Alistair in Outer Space
Amelia Bedelia Goes Camping
Anna's Secret Friend
Arthur's Tooth
The Bear's Bicycle
Caps for Sale
Clifford the Big Red Dog
Clifford the Small Red Puppy
Corduroy
Curious George
Curious George Goes Fishing
The Day Jimmy's Boa Ate the Wash
Doctor De Soto
Fox All Week
Frog and Toad Are Friends
George and Martha Back in Town
George Stinks
Gregory, The Terrible Eater
Happy Birthday, Ronald Morgan!
Harry the Dirty Dog
Henry and Mudge in the Puddle Trouble
Imogene's Antlers
Jafta—The Journey
Julius
Make Way for Ducklings
Miss Nelson is Missing
Nate the Great
No Roses for Harry
Pig Pig Goes to Camp
Pinkerton, Behave!
Shy Charles
The Snowy Day
Stega Nona
The Trek
There's Something in the Attic
We Can't Sleep
A Weekend with Wendell

Book II
Alexander and the Terrible, Horrible,
   No Good, Very Bad Day
Amelia Bedelia
Angela's Airplane
Arthur's Eyes
Bear Shadow
Clifford's Family
Clifford at the Circus
Clifford Gets a Job
Cloudy with a Chance of Meatballs
Could Be Worse
Curious George Goes to the Hospital
Danny and the Dinosaur
The Day the TV Blew Up
Even the Moose Won't Listen to Me
Fox at School
George and Martha One Fine Day
The Giving Tree
Guess Who My Favorite Person Is
Harry by the Sea
Henry and Mudge
The Horse in Harry's Room
Ira Sleeps Over
Jafta
Little Bear
Maggie and the Pirate
Miss Nelson is Back
My New Boy
Noisy Nora
Pet Show
Pig Pig Grows Up
Ronald Morgan Goes to Bat
A Rose for Pinkerton
Rotten Ralph
Sheila Rae, the Brave
Sylvester and the Magic Pebble
There's An Alligator Under My Bed
Where the Wild Things Are
Whistle for Willie

Book III
Alexander, Who Used to Be Rich
   Last Sunday
Alistair's Elephant
Amos and Boris
Arthur Goes to Camp
Arthur's Great Big Valentine
Best Friends
Chester's Way
Clifford and the Grouchy Neighbors
Clifford's Pal
Curious George Flies a Kite
The Day the Teacher Went Bananas
Family Farm
The Girl Who Loved Wild Horses
Grandpa's Face
The Great White Man-Eating Shark
Harry and the Terrible Whatzit
Hey, Al
How I Captured a Dinosaur
Jim Meets the Thing
Just Me and the Babysitter
Kate Shelley and the Midnight Express
The Legend of the Indian Paintbrush
Let's Go Swimming with Mr. Sillypants
Lon Po Po
Miss Nelson Has a Field Day
The One in the Middle Is the Green
   Kangaroo
Owl at Home
A Pocket for Corduroy
The Real Hole
Rotten Ralph's Show and Tell
Sammy the Seal
The Story of Ferdinand
Tales of Oliver Pig
Teammates
This Is My Friend
The Wild Baby Gets a Puppy

All paperback books listed are available and we will gladly order. Please contact us for prices.

Toll-Free Fax: 877.688.3226 • Phone: 800.688.3224

Get Writing!!

By Leif Fearn and Nancy Farnan

Finally! The complete teacher-friendly **Balanced Writing** program you've been looking for—not just another series of activity books.

- The creators of the **Balanced Writing** instruction curriculum now offer the book version of their prestigious writing program.

- Beginning with the acknowledgement that, "The great American novel is written one sentence at a time," the *Get Writing!!* series details procedures and activities for teaching K-5 students to formulate words into well-developed paragraphs.

- Balanced Writing instruction focuses specific attention on balancing content, process, and time components of writing with learning to write well. The result is a successful and teacher-friendly method to turn students into mature writers.

- Balanced Writing instruction has been successfully used in public, private, and home schooling environments for many years and is considered by many teachers to be THE way to teach writing instruction.

"I'm so glad I found you. Your company's products are great." OH

Features

- Every book contains overviews and objectives for each lesson, bulleted procedures for conducting each lesson, and daily activities.
- Applications for across-the-curriculum and applications for English language learners are included.
- Corresponding reproducible student activity sheets for each lesson are provided.
- Each book contains assessment procedures for evaluating student's progress.
- Month-long and year-long calendars and instructions for incorporating the curriculum into lesson plans will save you valuable planning time.

ECS 2231	**Easy Order Set of All 6 Books**		**$95.75**
ECS1928	Sentences	Gr. K	$13.95
ECS1936	Sentences & Paragraphs	Gr. 1	$15.95
ECS1944	Book 1: Sentences & Mechanical Control	Gr. 2-3	$15.95
ECS1952	Book 2: Paragraphs & Forms of Writing	Gr. 2-3	$17.95
ECS1960	Book 1: Main Ideas in Sentences	Gr. 4-5	$16.95
ECS1979	Book 2: Main Ideas in Paragraphs	Gr. 4-5	$16.95

Toll-Free Fax: 877.688.3226 • Phone: 800.688.3224

Structures for
Reading • Writing • Thinking

by Jo Anne Piccolo

A step-by-step and easy-to-learn method to help students bridge the gap between narrative stories and content-area text

Finally, a comprehensive teaching program for improving students' reading, writing, and thinking skills utilizing **expository text structures**.

Expository text structures are the organizational patterns that authors use to present ideas and to achieve a particular purpose in a single paragraph or entire text. Once a student has learned the expository text structures concepts, their ability to organize their thinking and write content-area text is greatly enhanced.

Each lesson is clearly organized and fully explained. Structures books are especially helpful for teachers who need alternatives to teaching paragraph skills and report writing. Consistent, easy-to-use format saves teachers valuable preparation time.

Features

• Each book includes teacher lesson plans with corresponding graphic organizers, rubrics, and reproducible student activity sheets.

• The appendices include graphic organizers, scoring rubrics, checklists, word maps, model paragraphs and reports, and reference handbook in Books 1 and 2.

• **Book 1**—expository text structures and three types of paragraphs: sequential, enumerative, and descriptive. **Book 2**—expository text structures and three types of paragraphs: compare/contrast, cause/effect, and problem/solution. **Book 3**—research and report writing. **Book 4**—content-area reading and writing.

• **Reproducible teacher/student activity sheets are included.**

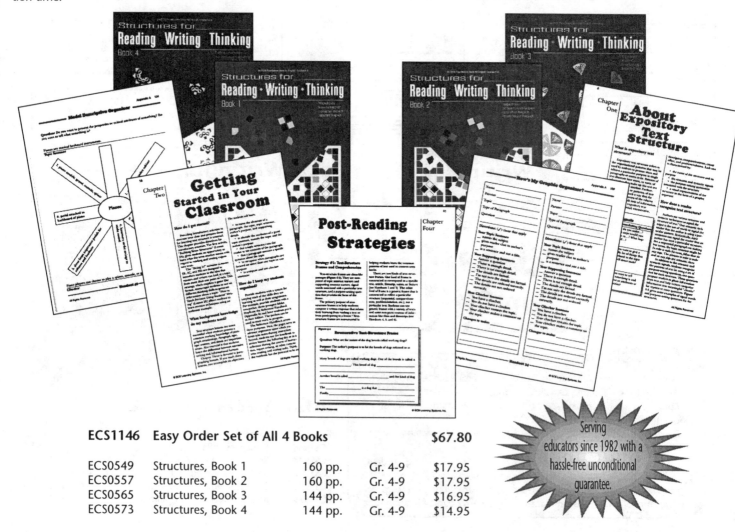

ECS1146	Easy Order Set of All 4 Books			$67.80
ECS0549	Structures, Book 1	160 pp.	Gr. 4-9	$17.95
ECS0557	Structures, Book 2	160 pp.	Gr. 4-9	$17.95
ECS0565	Structures, Book 3	144 pp.	Gr. 4-9	$16.95
ECS0573	Structures, Book 4	144 pp.	Gr. 4-9	$14.95

Toll-Free Fax: 877.688.3226 • Phone: 800.688.3224

ECS TestSMART™

Establishing a NEW standard for state competency test resources

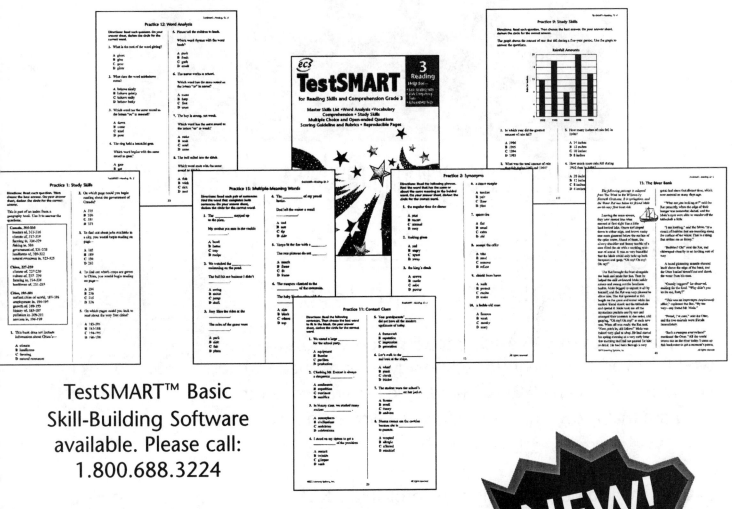

TestSMART™ Basic Skill-Building Software available. Please call: 1.800.688.3224

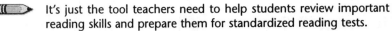
It's just the tool teachers need to help students review important reading skills and prepare them for standardized reading tests.

ECS TestSMART™ contains reproducible practice exercises for word analysis, vocabulary, comprehension, and study skills.

Extensive master skills list represents a synthesis of reading skills from all the major test specifications and can easily be correlated from one state to another.

Scoring guidelines and sample rubrics are provided for evaluating responses to open-ended questions. Answer keys are provided for all multiple-choice questions.

ECS TestSMART™ helps students become familiar with both the content and format of state competency tests.

ECS1987	Reading	128pp.	Gr. 3	$16.95
ECS1995	Reading	128pp.	Gr. 4	$16.95
ECS2002	Reading	128pp.	Gr. 5	$16.95
ECS2010	Reading	128pp.	Gr. 6	$16.95
ECS2029	Reading	128pp.	Gr. 7	$16.95
ECS2037	Reading	128pp.	Gr. 8	$16.95